LaSALLE *and the Grand Enterprise*

P. René Cavelier de
La Salle ☩ De La Salle

D

<u>ASIN</u>

B0007FLV6K

LaSALLE

and the

GRAND ENTERPRISE

JEANNETTE COVERT NOLAN

JULIAN MESSNER, INC.   NEW YORK

PUBLISHED BY JULIAN MESSNER, INC.
8 WEST 40TH STREET, NEW YORK 18.
PUBLISHED SIMULTANEOUSLY IN CANADA
BY THE COPP CLARK COMPANY, LTD.
COPYRIGHT 1951, BY JEANNETTE COVERT NOLAN.

PRINTED IN THE UNITED STATES OF AMERICA

CONTENTS

CHAPTER		PAGE
I	Plan for Adventure	1
II	"Welcome to America!"	15
III	The Forest Seigniory	25
IV	The First Excursion	38
V	New Friends, New Prospects	47
VI	The Grand Enterprise	58
VII	The Northern Winter	68
VIII	Forts in the Wilderness	78
IX	The Search	92
X	"In the King's Name!"	103
XI	Report to Paris	112
XII	Voyage in Strange Waters	123
XIII	The Wide Blue Gulf	133
XIV	The Difficult Days	140
XV	Journey Eastward	148
XVI	Fateful Morning	157
XVII	Epilogue	165
Bibliography		173
Index		175

LaSALLE *and the Grand Enterprise*

Journeys of La Salle

Route 1 •—•—• 1669
Route 2 ————— 1671-72-82
Route 3 •••••• 1684-85-86-87

PLAN FOR ADVENTURE

I

SIDE by side the young man and the old priest walked toward the high iron fence which bordered the school-yard. The young man was tall; his legs were long; to keep step, the priest must hurry a bit, the skirts of his rough wool robe disturbed by a brisk wind blowing inshore from the river Seine.

It was the last afternoon of February, 1666, still winter, still quite cold. Father Guiscard shivered slightly.

"This bright sunshine is deceptive, Robert," he said. "The season has not yet changed."

Robert Cavelier smiled and said nothing; he was thinking that by the time the season changed he might be hundreds, even thousands, of miles from here. At the gate which opened upon the busy Rouen street, he paused and glanced back. He might never again see the big gray stone building to which he had come daily, as a pupil first, then as an instructor, for most of his twenty-two years of life—but his blue eyes were unshadowed by regret.

He had learned much at the Jesuit school. Yes, and for a while he had actually felt that to study Greek, Latin, mathematics, geography, to preside over a classroom of other learners, perhaps later to become a Jesuit himself, might be his true career.

"Now I am glad to leave," he thought. "Very glad. Jean's letters from Canada have made me realize all I've been missing. It's only the farewells that will be difficult, the partings from home, relatives, and good friends —like this one."

Father Guiscard knotted the cord belt of his robe and laid a hand on Robert's arm. "I can guess what's in your mind."

"Can you, sir?"

"You are impatient to begin the great adventure."

"The adventure may seem mad to you—"

"Oh, no!" Father Guiscard said. "Not to me. On the contrary, I have often watched groups of my fellow Jesuits start forth for the New World—and wished I might go with them, carrying God's word to the far corners of earth. But I have not been called; it was not the will of my superiors. So I have remained, a teacher— in Rouen."

Robert thought: "That's just why I could never have been a member of any religious community! I haven't the disposition; I've got to follow my own will, not someone else's!" . . . Of course it was not a thing to say, especially to a gentle old man who loved him.

"You sail on the next ship for America?" asked Father Guiscard, out of the little silence.

"Yes, sir. The date is uncertain. It may be a week off, or a month."

"And you go to Quebec?"

"Yes, where my brother Jean will meet me. I suppose you have heard of my brother?"

"The Abbé Jean Cavalier, a priest of St. Sulpice? I have, indeed, heard of him."

"He is at Montreal. The Sulpicians have a seminary there and much land, given them by King Louis, which they are parceling out to be colonized."

"As the Jesuits are colonizing in other regions of New France," said Father Guiscard.

Robert continued: "By Jean's report Canada is a wonderful place, filled with splendid lakes and forests, rivers and mountains—"

"And hordes of warlike red Indians to be fought, eh?"

"Indians, yes. But I shall not fight them," Robert said. "I'll clear and cultivate any land the Sulpicians allot me; and if Indians are on it, let them stay—I'll cultivate them too!"

"Bravo! Excellent!" Father Guisard chuckled. "That method of dealing with barbarians is frequently overlooked."

Beyond the fence, in the town, the cathedral bell

tolled four o'clock, and was echoed by bells in all the spires of Rouen's many churches.

Robert counted the strokes. "I must be off," he said. "Today my Uncle Henri visits us. Since my father's death Uncle Henri has managed our family's estate and affairs. As a mere formality, I must have his consent to my plans."

"You're sure you will obtain it?"

"Quite sure."

"And your mother? She is not dismayed?"

"I think she may be, a little," Robert said slowly. "But my mother wants me to be happy—"

"So do we all!" Father Guiscard exclaimed. "And you were not happy in our pious company. I saw it— saw how you struggled against the dull routine, the confinement, the sensation of being hemmed in by rules, doors, walls, this fence!"

Robert hesitated, his hand on the latch of the gate. "You are very understanding, sir, very kind. I—I hope you'll pray for me."

"Depend upon it," said Father Guiscard. "Yes, I'll pray for your health, your success. I'll pray that God will bless you and guard you from the sin of ambition."

"But is ambition a sin?"

"In small doses, perhaps not. Sometimes, though," said Father Guiscard, "as a man ages and succeeds, he loses the genius to distinguish between ambition which leads to worthy ends and that which only satisfies personal selfishness. Ah, well, forgive me, Robert! Mine is the caution of an old fellow who has had scant experience—and no ambition at all. You know that I admire and trust you?"

"I know that your trust will never be betrayed, sir," said Robert earnestly.

As the gate swung, they clasped hands.

"Good-by," Father Guiscard said.

"No! *Au 'voir!*" said Robert.

Then the latch fell and clicked; the gate was shut.

Out in the street Robert walked rapidly. Everything was familiar to him—the rows of shops; the public buildings, the Hôtel de Ville and Palais de Justice; the Tour de Jeanne d'Arc, where the sainted Maid of Orleans had been tried and martyred; the wooden bridges spanning narrow runnels which thrust up, like fingers, from the river into the town.

He knew Rouen, each nook and corner of it, for he had been born here; yes, and his father, his grandfathers, before him. The Caveliers were city dwellers, burghers; they owned farms in Normandy and, by French custom, borrowed the names of such farms as titles for their sons. Thus, Robert Cavelier was the Sieur de La Salle—

"But I've seldom seen the farm of La Salle, or any farm," he thought. "How strange that, having lived always in the city, I now should yearn to plunge into the wildest of wildernesses!"

At the water front he stopped. The wind was blowing strong and free; it billowed his quilted damask cape, ruffled the light brown hair which curled on his shoulders. Small boats, dories, fishing smacks, and barges were roped to the moorings, but no vessels of size, none which might have crossed the ocean, to lie at the Rouen wharves, refreighting for the return voyage.

He must wait—and to wait was tedious; he seemed to lack the talent for it. As Father Guiscard had remarked, he was impatient.

Sighing, he faced about and, with the wind at his back, went on, up another street, over a wooden bridge, homeward.

The Cavelier house was large and fine, made half of sturdy brown timbers, half of plaster painted white, with peaked gables, diamond-paned windows, and a walled garden in the rear. The front door, with polished brass knocker and knob, was flush with the cobbled pavement. As Robert neared, the door flew open and out tumbled a very small fair-haired boy with jelly stains on his cheeks and a soiled bib under his chin.

"Crevel!" Robert cried. "What are you doing?"

"Running away!" The little boy hurled himself at Robert, grasped him around the knees.

"Running away? Where?"

"To Canada!"

"Ah?" Stooping, Robert lifted Crevel in his arms. "And what does your mother say to that?"

"*Maman* says—"

Robert's sister, Marie Cavelier de Moranget, appeared on the threshold and stepped toward her son.

"I say he is naughty!" Marie declared. "Yes, and you also, Robert. I must scold you both, Crevel for escaping from Nurse Elise, you for being late."

"Am I late, then?"

"Very," Marie said. "The family is in the parlor; Uncle Henri has consented to your journey—we are deciding your fate."

"But my fate is decided. And Crevel tells me he has decided his; he's going to Canada—"

"Crevel is going to the nursery, to have his face washed!"

"I'm going to Canada!" Crevel now was clinging to the collar of Robert's cape. "With *you*! I want to—I want to—"

"Well, so you shall, my pet!"

"Oh, Robert, hush!" Marie exclaimed. "He'll remember. He'll believe that you mean it."

"I do mean it. Yes," Robert said, "someday my nephew Crevel and I will travel together to America. La Salle and de Moranget! But it'll not be until he has grown much bigger and fatter, and eaten jars of jelly, and had his face washed— Ah, here's Elise!"

"Thank heavens! Take him! Take the boy, Elise." Marie turned to the elderly nursemaid who approached, padding on carpet-slippered feet. "He's sticky!"

"And sweet," said Robert.

"And stubborn," said Elise. "Stubborn as a donkey—like you, sir."

"So! This is what you think of me, Elise?"

The woman grinned. "I've thought it since you were in swaddling clothes."

"I'm going to Canada," Crevel announced triumphantly. "When I'm big and fat, and have had my face washed."

"I don't doubt it," said Elise. "You're more Cavelier than de Moranget—and the Caveliers will have their way or die!"

Marie and Robert went into the parlor, a spacious room, furnished with quiet elegance. As they entered, Marie's husband, Monsieur de Moranget, rose and placed a chair for her. Madame Cavelier and her youngest son, Paul, were seated on a divan beneath the window. Robert bent and kissed his mother's forehead, heartily shook Paul's hand, then turned to his Uncle Henri who sat at a table with papers spread out before him.

"I must apologize for my tardiness," Robert said.

Madame Cavelier smiled. Slender, dignified, and erect, she was dressed in black silk with a scarf of cream-colored lace pinned over her graying hair.

"The delay is of no consequence," she said.

"Except," said Paul, "that in your absence we talked about you—as we couldn't have done, otherwise."

"Yes, Robert." Uncle Henri glanced up from his papers. "Have a chair. There are things to be discussed here—important things."

Robert nodded and made himself comfortable in a cushioned chair. Uncle Henri was a merchant, a man of business, as Robert's father had been. He wore the plainest sort of garments, a suit of olive-drab, a linen neckerchief, horn-rimmed spectacles astride his long, thin nose, a neat black skullcap on his bald head. Though fond of Uncle Henri, Robert often was bored with him.

"He is deliberate as a snail," Robert thought, "and when he mentions 'important things' it's sure to be money."

So it was today. Uncle Henri had brought a list of the various properties which he managed for Madame Cavelier. Slowly and distinctly, in his businesslike manner, he read the list. This was the family wealth, inherited by Madame Cavelier at her husband's death.

"In normal circumstances, and in time, Madame Cavelier's holdings would have been divided in equal shares among her four children. That is what my brother expected—what anyone would have expected. But," said Uncle Henri, peering over the rims of his glasses, "the circumstances have proved to be *not* normal. Jean Cavelier, by joining the Sulpician priesthood a few years ago, forfeited the right to his one-fourth share. And René Robert Cavelier, Sieur de La Salle, by lingering on with the Jesuits, teaching at their school and toying with the idea of becoming a priest of that order, has forfeited *his* right."

Robert yawned behind his hand.

"This," said Uncle Henri, "is the law. I have consulted with the best lawyers in Rouen; I have written to lawyers in Paris. All opinions are the same. Yes, as mat–

ters now seem to stand, Marie Cavelier de Moranget and Paul Cavelier are the sole future heirs to the fortune now held and enjoyed by their mother. When the Sieur de La Salle embarks for America, it will be with the knowledge that—*legally*—he is penniless."

Uncle Henri paused and looked sternly at Robert.

"The old codger is annoyed with me," Robert thought. "He doesn't fancy this dangerous excursion abroad to seek my own fortune—which, he imagines, I'm not likely to find. He would rather I had remained with the Jesuits; another priest in the family would add honor to the Cavelier name. Or, better, he wishes I'd be a merchant, as he is, and Marie's husband, as Paul is training to be. But I won't—and he knows it!"

There was a brief silence in the parlor. Then Uncle Henri said: "A penniless Cavelier? Most unusual!"

Robert stirred in his chair; he shrugged. "The prospect does not frighten me. I've never put undue value on wealth—"

"Because you've never been without it," said Uncle Henri. "Wandering, penniless, in America? You would be wretched. You might even starve."

"Oh, no!" Now Robert was annoyed. "No, sir!"

"Yes," insisted Uncle Henri. "Therefore it has been agreed that you must have an allowance, paid annually from the estate."

"An allowance? Who has agreed to that?"

"Your mother, Marie, Paul—and I."

Robert stared in amazement. They were all smiling at him—except Uncle Henri; he was frowning.

"You are very generous," Robert said. "But I could not accept the allowance."

"Nonsense! You must accept it." Uncle Henri pounded his fist on the table. "Why, I've drawn a paper, a *legal* paper, which we have signed. Accept the allowance—or fling it into the sea!"

Marie interrupted. "The amount is small, Robert. A pittance. My husband and I think it should have been more."

"I think it should have been lots more," said Paul.

"As for me"—Uncle Henri frowned and shuffled his papers—"I think Robert is trotting off on a fool's errand. But if he is determined—"

"Robert is quite determined, Henri." Madame Cavelier got to her feet; somehow her low-pitched voice stilled the tumult of the other voices. "He has made his choice, as it was his privilege to do. But he will accept the allowance, if only for my sake. And we shall have no further debating of any kind!"

Madame Cavelier walked to the parlor door, which Monsieur de Moranget sprang to open for her.

"Henri, you will stay for dinner," she said. "Marie, see that a plate is set for your uncle. Monsieur de Moranget, you will help Paul select a bottle of wine from the cellar. And you, Robert, will want a minute's rest before the meal."

He went into the hall, toward the staircase. It was
dark; the lamps had not yet been lighted. At the left of
the stairs was a deep embrasure which, on winter nights
like this, was curtained by a heavy tapestry hanging
from the ceiling to the floor. Now the curtain seemed
to bulge and, with an impetuous gesture, Robert jerked
it aside to reveal a figure crouching there.

"Ah, Peter Saget!" Robert said. "Eavesdropping?"

"Napping, sir."

"Well, get up. Go up to my room."

The figure unfolded, stood, climbed the staircase; and
Robert followed. From the upper hall they went into a
bedroom where candles burned on the bureau. Robert
lay down on the bed, regarding Peter Saget. Seen by
candlelight, the youth was short and stocky, sallow-
complexioned, with a bristle of black hair and eyes as
bright and black as a squirrel's. He wore a servant's
black bombazine jacket, black trousers and leather
apron.

"My work is tiresome," Saget said, fidgeting under
Robert's scrutiny. "Why, I slave from morning till
night, in the stables, the garden, the kitchen—"

"Slave? You are the laziest lout in Rouen."

Saget ignored the comment. "But I'll not be so over-
worked when I go to Canada with you, sir."

"Indeed?" Robert said. "Many people would like to
go to Canada with me. My nephew Crevel—"

"That infant! Crevel is not yet dry behind the ears. I,
sir, am not a baby!"

"How old are you, Saget?"

"Oh, eighteen—or twenty; I don't know. At an orphanage they're not particular about birthdays, and when you can fend for yourself they just shove you out. So it was with me, sir. Perhaps you recollect that morning five years ago?" Saget wagged his dark head. "I was very hungry; I had snatched an apple from the fruit peddler's cart. One little wrinkled apple! Who would have thought the peddler would yell so loud? He chased me; the police came. Then you drove by in your grand carriage, tossing silver coins to the peddler, the police, bidding me to get into the carriage. And you drove me to this house, where I've been ever since, serving you— faithful as a dog."

"But not treated like a dog. In this house you've lived like a respectable human being, with plenty to eat, good wages—"

"Oh, I don't complain, sir. Or, anyway, not much, not often. It's not in my nature to complain. I'm very brave, as you will see when I go with you to Canada."

Robert laughed. "You're very wily, Peter. But I can't take you."

"You'll need a valet."

"In that primitive country? No, Peter."

"You'll need a protector. What your uncle said is so. You've been rich, sheltered, everything soft and easy for you."

"I'll hire an Indian."

"An Indian?" Saget shuddered. "And have him kill

you the first night? Slit your gullet as you sleep? Those Indians are cruel, bloodthirsty. I've read about them in books. I am the perfect protector for you, sir, none better!"

"But I fear my mother couldn't spare you," Robert said teasingly. "A person of such modesty and intelligence."

"Yes, Madame Cavelier will miss me. She said that."

Robert sat up. "You have asked her?"

"Could I have gone without asking her?"

"Peter," Robert said. "I'm stubborn, proud; I have a bad temper, a sharp tongue. You would find me a hard master—"

Saget smiled tolerantly. "You're the only master I want, sir. I will pardon your faults."

"WELCOME TO AMERICA!"

II

ONE March morning in 1666 Robert stood at the stern rail of a small merchant vessel just ready to weigh anchor from the Rouen wharf.

It was a moment of tension, all the cargo and passengers aboard, the hatches battened, the crew busily regulating the sheets to catch a freshening wind, the helmsman in position under the steerage's vaulted hood.

Beneath his scarlet velvet cloak Robert's heart pounded with excitement; the hand which rested on his sword hilt was trembling in its embroidered glove.

Looking down over the rail, beyond the angle of the ship's lantern, he could see his brother Paul, his sister Marie, her husband, and little Crevel on the pier. They had come to wish him *bon voyage*. But his mother was not there.

"She wouldn't come," Marie had said. "She shrank from watching you vanish into the unknown."

"Well, it is better so," Robert agreed. "Will you, Marie, tell her good-by again, for me?"

"Oh, yes!"

"La Salle, do not fret about Madame Cavelier," said Monsieur de Moranget. "With all of us to care for her, she'll want for nothing."

"I'm sure of that," said Robert.

Now the white sails swelled from the three masts; anchor chains clanked; ropes whined. The ship quivered with life.

Robert swept off his high-crowned, plumed hat and waved it. He blew a kiss to Marie, a kiss to Crevel.

"Someday *I* am going," Crevel shouted, his voice a shrill, childish treble. "Someday—"

"Yes, yes!" Robert replied. "Someday!"

The ship moved, widening the strip of water between stern and wharf. The figures on the pier dwindled; when they were no bigger than dolls, Robert stepped from the half-deck to the waist, where Peter Saget sat perched on a pile of luggage.

"We're starting, sir," said Saget.

"Yes, but you could get back to Rouen—by swimming."

"In these clothes? No, sir!" said Saget emphatically. "Why, they're the most stylish I've ever had, decent black cloth, like a gentleman's. Do you see my cap?"

"A sailor's cap, isn't it? Very nice."

"And I have one for you, sir, packed in the satchel. Better put it on; the gale will tear your plumes to shreds."

"Fetch me the cap, then," Robert said, "and swing our hammocks. I'll introduce myself to the captain."

The ship glided smoothly with wind and tide up the Seine, into and through the English Channel, then into the Atlantic Ocean. For several days the weather was bland, the sea calm; cottony clouds flecked a soft blue sky.

Having made the captain's acquaintance, Robert soon introduced himself to the other passengers. There were not many of these; few people except professional sailors had the hardihood for such a long voyage. Besides the Sieur de La Salle and his servant, Saget, the travelers were ten in number: three Recollet friars, or Franciscans; four stalwart bearded men who had been soldiers in the French army; a young married couple with a tiny baby. All were quartered in a windowless cabin below the waist of the ship, with individual sleeping compartments devised by the stringing of canvas panels on cords suspended from the ceiling. They ate their meals together, cooking the food on a small stove and eating at a common table over which a swaying oil lamp threw a feeble glow.

Saget said that the accommodations were abominable; the stove emitted more smoke than heat, the lamp smoked, and both had the foulest smell.

"Like a rat hole! And I do think you look very out of place here, sir. That scarlet cloak will get dirty. Let me fold it away. But why did you bring it at all? The cloak is a civilized thing—and we've put civilization behind us forever, haven't we?"

Robert took off the scarlet velvet. "Fold it nicely. I may wear it later."

"When?" asked Saget, surprised. "Where?"

"Oh, there may be a time," said Robert.

The ship's captain also seemed to think that this youthful Sieur de La Salle was somewhat out of place in the "rat hole." The captain invited him to bunk in the forecastle. But Robert refused, courteously. He was not bothered by the cabin's hodgepodge of human beings, its stuffiness, smoke, and smells; and he enjoyed the contact with his fellow emigrants.

They were all hopeful for what was in store for them as permanent residents of Canada.

The Recollet friars hoped to convert the Indians. The four soldiers would be fur trappers; they hoped to snare myriads of furry little beasts, send the pelts to European markets, and reap enormous profits. The young married couple hoped for a new home in the New World for themselves, the baby, and any more children they might have hereafter.

But what did the Sieur de La Salle hope for in Canada? What would he do?

"I'll go on from Quebec to Montreal with my brother."

And then what?

"I don't know," he said. "My brother has plans for me."

Sometimes he played a game of piquet with the captain on the half-deck. The stakes were low, for he had not many gold pieces to wager. In his purse was his allowance for this year. As Marie had observed, it was a pittance—and on the morning of sailing, Paul had nudged him and whispered:

"If you're ever strapped, Robert, call on the Caveliers. Your relatives aren't misers."

"Uncle Henri?"

"No," Paul said. "Not even Uncle Henri!"

The captain had considerable knowledge of America; dealing the cards, he spoke of how vast and various it was, how no one could accurately estimate either its size or its shape, for only the east coast had been settled— and this but a short distance inland.

All the nations of old and overpopulated Europe were competing desperately for territory in America. The Spaniards had Mexico and were pushing inward; the Dutch were on the Hudson River; the English indefatigably colonized in Virginia, Massachusetts, and Connecticut.

The captain spoke of Canada: by right of Jacques Cartier's discoveries, it was the possession of France; and in 1608 Samuel de Champlain had founded Quebec as the capital of New France. Indeed, Champlain had been Canada's immortal hero. Though once compelled to surrender his beloved Quebec, he had survived to see the town and the country restored to France.

"And it must remain French!" said the captain, adding that France was the greatest nation in all Christendom, that the colonizing of Canada was a joint endeavor of the noble King and the holy Church.

Robert played his cards slowly, more absorbed in the conversation than in the piquet.

"We Frenchmen must find and lay claim to the Mississippi River in America," said the captain. "Ah, but how? That is the problem!"

"The Mississippi?" Robert said.

"An Indian name for the Indians' river of mystery. Mississippi, Father of Waters, so big that it seems the parent of all other streams. You perhaps have examined an oak leaf and noticed its skeleton? One strong central spine from which branch off many small ribs. That spine is the Mississippi! Or maybe I should say that it is the main artery from the heart of America, sustaining the continent's whole body."

"Isn't the Mississippi Hernando de Soto's river?" Robert asked.

"Yes, but the Spaniard De Soto saw it over a century ago, and only its upper reaches. No white man has seen it since. De Soto was buried in the Mississippi. They tell that, as he was dying, he commanded his followers to cast his corpse into the water's depths. And they did."

"I should like to see this river," Robert said thoughtfully.

The captain chuckled. "Have a care, sir, or you'll get explorer's fever, an insidious disease which creeps into a man's blood and can't be cured."

"Explorer's fever?" Robert repeated, more thoughtfully still.

In the night a storm struck; the ship pitched and wallowed in the trough of wicked green waves, and for two weeks was tossed about like a spinning cork. Robert was sick; all occupants of the lower cabin were hideously sick; and when the storm subsided, the wind went with it. For fifteen days the ship listed idly.

One by one the invalids recovered; groaning, they staggered up to the deck where they could spread their blankets to the air and feel the April sun on their pallid faces. Captain and crew scanned the sky for signs of a reviving wind. The Recollet friars prayed soberly, pacing back and forth in their gray mendicants' gowns, reading their breviaries, saying the rosary.

On the sixteenth day a breeze whispered, then stretched the sails; the ship plied westward.

The travelers, who before had talked of America, seemed now to be persistently reminded of France and all they had left in the past. Perhaps, Robert thought, this was the reaction from illness; or perhaps they were realizing the ocean's ominous width, the gravity of the step they were taking.

"No," Saget said. "They begin to be frightened of the red savages in America. And why not? I myself would rather talk of French cities, French ways—the King." . . .

Louis XIV, what a magnificent king he was! The *Grand Monarque*, and everything a monarch should be,

regal, imperious, maintaining a court which was a para-
dise of pleasure, the most brilliant in Europe—a court
other kings might imitate but never equal.

Ah, he was powerful, too, a law unto himself. None
dared oppose him, not even his ministers; for he would
as quickly punish a minister as lash out with his riding
whip at some yapping dog. The sun was his emblem; it
was as the sun that he liked to picture himself:

Louis XIV; Louis, the sun, round, golden, beaming,
infusing all his people with light and warmth and vigorous life.

Yes, poverty did exist among these people; instances
of oppression and suffering were not unknown. A king,
to be so grand, so magnificent, must have funds, which
means the levying of taxes—taxes paid by endless labor
(though not, of course, the king's labor)—a ruler, to be
omnipotent, must tyrannize, which means that every
lesser man bends the knee in meek subjection. . . .

"Courcelle is Governor of Canada," said the ship's
captain, "and will be until the King supplants him with
someone else—the King is whimsical. Jean Talon is the
Governor's Intendant. You may meet Courcelle and
Talon."

"Oh, no!" Robert said. "I'll stop but briefly in Quebec; I'd have no reason to meet them."

It was May then, the last week of the month, and the
voyage almost done. The ship entered the Gulf of St.
Lawrence, an expanse of choppy, slate-colored water
ninety miles in breadth. Gulls skimmed above the masts,

screaming raucously, their wings like white pennants against the sky.

"I see land." Robert pointed to a black line, thin as a pencil stroke.

"That's Anticosti Island. We're in the river's estuary. If it weren't for the fog, you'd see crags to the north— the Laurentian mountains. Southward the hills are less rugged. Cartier discovered the St. Lawrence in 1543, not knowing at all what country he had chanced upon."

A huge dark promontory appeared to westward.

"There!" the captain said. "Quebec, the Rock. The fort is on the summit, the town below."

Robert peered at the Rock, which rose steep and sheer, with the turrets of the fort, a spiked crown, at its top. The streets of the town slanted upward in ledges and were walled with stone. From the river's edge a wide quay projected, with piers and platforms and a basin harboring dozens of boats.

"Why, this Quebec is a substantial city," Robert said as the gangplank was flung out. "It's not unlike Rouen."

"Oh, no!" said Saget. "Look at the people on the platform."

A crowd had collected to watch the vessel dock. Woodsmen, hunters, *coureurs de bois*, roughly clad, shrewd-visaged, with axes at their belts, guns in hand, they bore the unmistakable stamp of pioneer and trail blazer.

"You'd never find such folk at the Rouen wharf, sir,"

Saget said. "And Indians! See them? Copper-brown, half-naked, carrying tomahawks to scalp us with—"

But Robert was hastening down the gangplank.

"Jean! Jean!"

"Robert!" A priest disengaged himself from the crowd. "Robert, is it *you*?"

Amid the bustle of disembarking passengers the Abbé de Cavelier embraced his brother.

"Welcome! Welcome to America!" said Jean.

THE FOREST SEIGNIORY

III

THE two Cavelier brothers and Peter Saget went by canoe up the St. Lawrence. The day was crisp and sparkling; and Robert continually exclaimed at the beauty of the scenery, the dense forests green with spring foliage, the purplish-blue steeps of the Laurentians in the background. Occasionally the canoe passed Indian villages where dark-skinned children romped about ramshackle huts or conical tepees on the river bank, and lean, wolfish-looking hounds howled dismally.

Saget said that he had read of these natives; they were lazy and improvident, much given to feasting. When hunting, they killed many more animals than they could eat; gorged themselves with the meat, threw what remained to their dogs—and next morning, being hungry again, ate the dogs.

The Abbé Cavelier was wielding the paddle. He was

a man of thirty and, though not so muscular as Robert, he had broad shoulders beneath his priestly habit.

"Yes, Peter," he said, "they are a very brutal people. But now some are becoming Christianized. It's the wish of the King as well as of the Church that in time they will all be touched with the word of God."

Jean told of the Iroquois uprising which Governor Courcelle had just quelled. The Five Nations of Iroquois Indians, a confederacy of Mohawks, Oneidas, Onondagas, Cayugas, and Senecas, had attacked white settlers in the vicinity of Montreal, and had been repulsed.

"Courcelle has worked out a sort of peace with the chieftains," Jean said. "Alas, I fear it's only temporary. Montreal is probably the most dangerous spot in Canada, because of its exposed position—on an island, far from any other settlement. Montreal was at first a religious colony, an outpost of missionaries; but, to hold it, the government has had to fortify it as a military outpost too."

"In your letters you wrote that the authorities are trying to induce immigrants to come to live in Montreal," said Robert.

Jean nodded. "Yes, for the sake of security. It must be said that Canadian fur traders need no special inducement; they come of their own volition, and Montreal has grown to be a brisk center for the fur trade. But if the authorities can extend the boundaries of our town, they will be creating a little ring of Christian civilization in the pagan wilderness—and a barricade against the ferocious onslaughts of the Iroquois."

After an hour Saget took the paddle. Jean rested, and talked to Robert about their mother, the family and friends in Rouen whom he had not seen for years. But Robert was thinking of the Indians. Why was it, he asked, that white men here had so much bitter trouble with them?

"Here and everywhere," said Jean sadly. "I suppose a lack of understanding is at the bottom of it. White men and red do not speak the same language."

"Couldn't white men learn the Indian language?"

"Yes," said Jean. "Not many of them do so."

"Is it difficult, then?"

"Very; and there is no single language, but one for each of the big tribal divisions—and several dialects, besides."

"If the languages and dialects can be learned, I shall learn them," Robert declared. "Where can I get books?"

"Books of instruction? I know of none," Jean said. "Nika might teach you. Nika is a Christianized Shawnee, a man of character and some education. He has attached himself to the Seminary of St. Sulpice; you'll meet him."

"I'll ask Nika to be my tutor," said Robert. "Saget, give me the paddle; it's my turn to sweat."

"And I'll tell you what I have in mind for you," said Jean.

As the canoe pushed steadily upstream, Jean explained

his plan. The Sulpician Seminary was proprietor and feudal lord of Montreal; Father Queylus, the Seminary's Superior, strove tirelessly to further the interests of his Church and King. To the Sieur de La Salle, Father Queylus would gladly grant a tract of land on which to construct a town. This tract, many miles square, would be an extension of the Sulpicians' "little ring of Christian civilization," and a seigniory, or dominion, over which La Salle would have absolute control.

"Thus, Robert, you'll be doing your part in a splendid work," Jean said. "I have picked out the very place for your seigniory—nine miles south of Montreal, where the St. Lawrence widens to form the Lake of St. Louis."

Robert had been listening intently. "But, Jean, I have scarcely any money."

"Have you a medal of fine silver, the weight of one mark?"

"Yes. And that's nothing!"

"It's all you will owe Father Queylus. A token payment, one mark of silver delivered to the Seminary each year."

"But a town, Jean? How would I build it, how populate it?"

"You'd have to build it well; and if you did, there would be people to live in it. Fur trappers would come—"

"I'd like to be a trapper," said Saget, his dark eyes glinting. "Shall we have a fort at our seigniory, sir? And what can we name it?"

Robert smiled. "Not so fast, Peter," he admonished. "Let me accustom myself to the notion."

Montreal's one street ran parallel to the river and was lined with compact dwellings. At the end of the street was a bastioned fort sheltering a handful of troops, and a giant windmill with a stone foundation which could be utilized as a place of defense in time of siege. A large enclosure contained the fairly new hospital and the old buildings of the Seminary; the dormitory for the resident priests was also a guest house—and there, at the window of an upper room, Robert stood, looking out at the sunset.

Behind him, seated stiffly on a stool, was Nika, the Shawnee. For an hour the two men had been conferring. Nika's French was halting but adequate: yes, he knew seven or eight of the tribal tongues; yes, he would willingly teach the Sieur de La Salle, and they could commence at once.

With his finger he had indicated articles of the room's scant furnishings: the bed, a chair, a crucifix hanging on the wall, a cup on the window sill. Nika had supplied the Indian words; Robert had repeated the words after him.

"It will not be easy, I can see that," Robert had said.

"It is good that you wish to learn," said Nika.

Now the conference was over; Nika got up.

"One moment," Robert said. "Before you go, I would inquire of you—about a river in this country. De Soto's river, the Mississippi. You have heard of such a river?"

"Many times," answered Nika.

"Where are its headwaters? Through what regions does it flow, into what sea or ocean?"

"I do not know. I have never looked upon it. Some of the Jesuits, some *coureurs de bois*, claim to have seen it."

"Is it a route to Mexico, Japan, or China; a short cut to the Orient?"

"I do not know," said Nika again. "There are tales my people tell. But they are only tales."

"I would give a great deal for the opportunity to explore this river!"

"Many persons have dreamed of finding it." At the door Nika paused. "I will be your friend," he said solemnly.

"I will be grateful for your friendship," said Robert.

As the Indian left the room, Saget entered.

"Supper is downstairs in the refectory, sir."

"Thank you, Saget."

"I've been thinking about our seigniory. How wonderful to have a town of our own!"

"Yes—though we'll not have it immediately. The first task is one of clearing, and that's not done in a hurry. I must hire woodsmen to fell the trees, thousands of trees; Jean says the forest there is almost impenetrable. I must put up a main house, a fortress, an armory, and throw a palisade around them—and, as I told my brother, I have so little money!"

"But we'll be in the fur-trapping business."

"Yes. It will be our only source of revenue."

"Until the settlers come," Saget said. "Your tenants—you can charge them a high rent."

"A moderate rent. Token payments, like the mark of silver to Father Queylus. My tenants can pay me in cattle or fowls: a calf yearly, a few chickens, half a sou for each acre of the land—"

"Half a sou? Two cents, three? Sir, you shock me!" Saget exclaimed. "Why, you'll never get rich that way!"

"Suppose I don't want to get rich?"

"What, then, do you want?"

"I want, more than anything—well, no matter!" Robert said. "Let us eat our supper, Saget."

In less than a month a sizable segment of Canada's virgin timberland had been transferred to the ownership of the Sieur de La Salle, and axes were clashing in the forest nine miles south of Father Queylus's Seminary. Through the summer, through the brief, brilliant northern autumn, the work went forward. When winter breathed its first icy blasts, Robert could survey with satisfaction a circular clearing girdled by a thick-ribbed log palisade and centered by the blockhouse which was to be his home.

By mid-December he was living in the house, with Saget and Nika for company. It was terribly cold then; snow lay so deep that other tasks must be substituted for the labor of building. In Montreal, Robert had procured dozens of steel-jawed traps. With Nika, who was versed in such things, Saget distributed the traps on the shore of the river. Soon the outer walls of the blockhouse and the perpendicular surfaces of the palisade were tacked solidly with drying pelts—beaver, skunk, marten, musquash, here and there a silver fox, a blue fox, a silky lynx or wolverine.

However great the morning haul from the shiny new traps, more and more of the precious fur-bearing creatures were caught each night. Robert disliked the noise of their cries, so weird in the darkness; but to Saget this was music as pleasant as the jingling of gold coins.

"You have not a practical mind, sir."

"Perhaps not," said Robert.

Before Christmas the three men went back to Montreal with a sled full of furs, which they disposed of in the market. On Christmas Eve they attended the midnight mass celebrated by the Sulpicians in the Seminary. But they were at home in the blockhouse by Epiphany; Twelfth Night they celebrated alone, happily munching a bean cake which Saget had baked on the hearth, clinking their pewter mugs of wine and shouting the traditional toast:

"*To the King! The King drinks!*"

Winter was long; Robert had never known a season so relentlessly white and hushed, so frigid and bleak. He employed the indoor hours with study. Nika drilled him in the languages of the Indians, and he learned them— very slowly.

At last spring came; and settlers appeared, both red and white, for news had spread of La Salle's cheap rental rates. At the end of his first year as seignior Robert's tenants numbered thirty-seven, though of these nineteen were women and children.

The next autumn a band of Senecas straggled in and pitched camp for the winter. Robert was not sorry to have them. They interested him; all Indians interested him and he seemed to get on marvelously well with them, perhaps because he met them on a footing of dignity and equality.

The Senecas were storytellers. Some of them, the previous summer, had boated along a river which, they said, was not yet shown on any white man's map.

Listening, Robert pricked up his ears. Was this unmapped river the Father of Waters?

Ah, the Senecas said, it might be. Or, again, it might be the Ohio, a beautiful river rising in their own country, far to the south.

Robert's imagination flared. The Ohio? Did it flow to the "Vermilion Sea," the Gulf of California—to China? He prodded the Senecas for more information, but their stories lapsed into vagueness.

Nevertheless the vision of a beautiful, south-flowing river haunted him; and in the spring he announced to Saget his intention of going to Quebec, where he would talk with Governor Courcelle about an exploration of the Ohio.

Saget was nettled. "Our property here is developing

nicely, sir. Why must we set off on some wild goose chase?"

"*You* don't have to, Saget."

"Well, I'll not go with you to Quebec. But if you then turn into an explorer—you know, sir, that I would not fail my duty!"

"Is the St. Lawrence free of ice?" Robert asked.

"Almost," replied Saget, sighing. "Almost, sir."

Robert wore his scarlet cloak and plumed hat to Quebec. Striding into the Governor's office, he requested an audience with Courcelle and the Intendant, Jean Talon; and, having got that, he requested letters patent which would authorize his journey. Courcelle, he saw, as an aging man, beset with many vexations, at odds with Talon, weary of his responsibilities; Talon was younger, a politician who concealed his cleverness with the foppish airs of a courtier.

Courcelle said that he would grant the letters patent— but there was one obstacle:

"Funds, sir. Probably you can finance the scheme yourself?"

"No," Robert said. "What funds I had, and what I've made in furs, have been spent to defray the expenses of my seigniory."

"Yet you wish to leave this prosperous seigniory?"

"For a time, yes. Nika, my Shawnee friend, will look after it while I am away."

Courcelle thought for a moment. "You have improved your land; as it now stands, it should be valuable to the Sulpicians. Perhaps Father Queylus would buy back a part of it."

"Does the Sieur de La Salle know of the rivalry existing between the missionary groups in Canada?" asked Talon.

"Rivalry, sir?"

"The Jesuits," said Talon, "toil for the glorification of their order; the Franciscans, the Recollets, for the glory of France—"

"And the Sulpicians?" said Robert.

Talon smiled slyly. "The Sulpicians, I think, blend the two motives. But the Jesuits seem now to be outstripping the others, so it's not unlikely that Father Queylus would help you."

"I'll talk with him, then." Pausing, Robert added: "I had supposed that all priests toiled to convert the savages."

"They do," Talon said. "Ah, yes, they preach and pray. But they're all men, aren't they? Not angels. Ambitious, some of them—"

"As who is not?" said Courcelle, interrupting. "Monsieur Cavelier, you have my sanction of your exploration. Go and get Father Queylus's."

At the Seminary in Montreal, Robert saw Father Queylus, who was quite amiable.

"It's been suggested that I buy the land you have improved? I should prefer to lend you a fair sum. And I have a suggestion. By coincidence I've been thinking of sending missionaries into the Seneca country, and have

selected two priests for it. Father Dollier and Father
Galinée; they are Sulpicians. They can join you and
combine their aims with yours."

Robert thanked Father Queylus and went home—
where Saget said gloomily that the clergymen would be
more hindrance than help!

"They'll dictate to you."

"They will not! No one dictates to me, Saget."

Secretly, though, Robert was apprehensive. He had
wanted the party to be his; he could not envisage himself as second, or third, in command.

"Dollier was a captain of cavalry in France," com-
mented Saget. "He has the reputation of being very
highhanded."

"Probably that's said of me too. Be quiet, Saget!
Father Queylus has greatly accommodated me. It's only
right that I should now accommodate him."

Rather moodily Robert prepared for the journey.

"You're restless," remarked Jean Cavelier. "Were
you born a rover?"

"No, but I feel that I have work to do—for France."

The brothers were strolling around the seigniory
clearing.

"You're working for France here," Jean said.

"On a small scale, yes." Robert stopped and gestured.
"Jean, I've been in Canada long enough to know that
colonizing of any importance can scarcely be done in
this severe climate. Frenchmen must open up the interior
of America. We must have colonies to the south, where

there is more sunshine. Other nations are establishing such colonies—the English, the Dutch and Spanish—but France is lagging behind!"

"We have the Canadian fur trade; that's valuable."

"Yes. But to endure we must have homes, farms, fields, grazing pastures—and people who can thrive and grow, without the perpetual fear of being frozen to death!"

"So," Jean said, "it's for patriotic reasons that you're going to look for the Seneca's Ohio, *la belle riviere?*"

"Perhaps I'm only curious," Robert answered. "Curious to see the wonders of nature before anyone else has seen them. Or perhaps I'm thinking of that fence there."

"Your palisade?"

"I hated the fence at the school in Rouen. I hate this one."

Jean laughed. "Fences are useful. They keep out enemies."

"And keep me in," said Robert. "I loathe them all!"

THE FIRST EXCURSION

IV

At noon, July 6, 1669, seven birch-bark canoes slid out from the Sieur de La Salle's jetty into the St. Lawrence. Riding in the canoes were Robert and Saget, Father Dollier and Father Galinée, and twenty robust Frenchmen from Montreal. Behind this little fleet were two pirogues in which rode six of Robert's Seneca guests who now would show the way to their tribal territory.

Despite Robert's misgivings the journey began auspiciously. The priests seemed docile and cheerful; the weather was fine; the boats responded with speed to the rhythmic swing of the paddles. Each day on the St. Lawrence brought its surprises: tumbling rapids, serene expanses resembling lakes, a thousand islands like green gems studding the belt of crystal water. Each night the party slept ashore under midsummer stars; and there was never a dearth of food, for, besides the fish and fowl which were always to be had, the Senecas had packed a dozen sacks of Indian corn that might be cooked as mush or bread.

On August 2 the canoes emerged from the river into an immense lake. Robert noted the date in his diary.

"This shall be known as Lake Ontario," he said.

Somewhat later a placid bay on Lake Ontario's south shore was sighted.

"Irondequoit Bay," he said. "We'll camp here."

As Saget broiled trout for the evening meal, three Indians came from the forest. Saget gestured to Robert, who went to greet them.

"We seek the Ohio River," he said. "Can you tell us where it is?"

The Ohio? The Indians stared blankly. But perhaps, they said, their chief could tell. Would not the white men go to their village, which was near by?

"Will your chief give us a guide?"

A guide? The Indians nodded assent.

Robert turned to Father Dollier. "If we can get a reliable guide, we'll be in luck."

"I'll not go to their village," said Father Dollier, glowering.

"Wait for me, then," said Robert. "I'm going."

Next day, with Saget, Father Galinée, and five other Frenchmen, Robert followed the Indians into the pine woods. They walked for hours, and reached at length a

large circle of bark-and-mud huts in the very depths of
the wilderness.

"This," said the Indians proudly, "is our village."

It was noisy and incredibly dirty, seething with con-
fusion. Tom-toms pounded, dogs yelped, naked children ran about; squaws stirred the cauldrons hung above
smoky fires. The coming of the white men created a
sensation; at once they were pounced upon and almost
overwhelmed with expressions of friendliness. The chief
was extravagantly hospitable, lodging them in the biggest of the huts. The children piled pumpkins and baskets of berries at their door. The squaws dipped into the
cauldrons and ladled out cups of steaming soup for the
visitors.

That evening there was an exhibition of native dancing, a sumptuous feast of boiled maize, nuts, sunflower
seeds—and something else.

"What is it, sir?" asked Saget, chewing.

"Baked dog, I think. Eat it," said La Salle.

"Ugh!" Saget groaned, gulped, and coughed.

"Eat it!"

"Yes, sir," said Saget sadly.

But the chief did not answer the white men's questions
about the Ohio. He was evasive, pretending not to understand, then hinting that they would certainly be destroyed by the tribes of that country.

"We want a guide," Robert said, again and again.

The chief only grunted and wagged his head.

For a week, a month, the feasting and dancing continued, unabating. Robert was baffled, Saget disgusted, Father Galinée frightened. Somehow, somewhere, the Indians were obtaining whisky; they were constantly drunk; the nights had become a sequence of drunken orgies. A prisoner from an enemy tribe was dragged in, manacled, and burned at the stake. Forced to witness the prisoner's torture and agonizing death, the Frenchmen began to suspect that they might be put to a similar ordeal.

"We're prisoners too," Saget said. "We'll be killed, unless we escape."

"But—can we escape?" quavered Father Galinée.

"We must!" said Robert.

They escaped one night when the revelry was at its noisiest. Slipping through the forest, Robert led his men to their comrades on Irondequoit Bay.

But now the Sulpicians were reproachful. Father Galinée said that, because of La Salle's detour to that squalid Indian village, much good time had been squandered upon bad savages who could never be Christianized.

"I knew it!" Father Dollier said. "As I laid eyes on them, I knew those fellows would abuse you!"

Robert's temper was provoked, and he thought that Father Queylus had been mistaken: "The priests' aims are not identical with mine. The combination is not a happy one."

The canoes coasted westward to Otinawatawa, a Huron town where the presiding chief was genuinely friendly.

"You are looking for the Ohio? I have a guide for you, a Shawnee captive. I give him to you as a slave," the chief said. "He will take you to the Ohio in six weeks!"

At Otinawatawa, Robert met Louis Joliet, a young Canadian who was acquiring fame as a fur trader, explorer, and *coureur de bois*. In Quebec and Montreal, Robert had heard of Joliet.

"How strange," he said as they shook hands, "that our paths should cross in this isolated spot."

Joliet had been on Lake Superior: "Talon sent me out to find the copper mines. Talon will be disappointed."

"You did not find them?"

"Not even a nugget of copper. But Talon will start me out on some other chore. He has so many notions, eh? Well, what have you seen, La Salle?"

Robert said that a week ago his party had passed the outlet of the Niagara River: "Our attention was roused by a tremendous roaring, like cannonade. The Falls of Niagara—but we didn't go up the river to see them; our Sulpicians thought we had not the time for that."

"A pity!" exclaimed Joliet. "The cataract is the most spectacular thing in the world! A horseshoe of crystal water dashing from great heights, rising in pillars of white spray and mist."

"Father Galinée wrote a description of the sound."

"Oh, the sound's the least of it!" Joliet seemed to muse. "I have a map of the Upper Lakes which your friars might care to see."

By the evening's firelight the Sulpicians looked at Joliet's map, and listened as he told them of the Pottawattami Indians around Lake Superior who, he said, were all heathens, craving conversion.

"Why do you not go and minister to the Pottawattamies?"

Father Dollier was enchanted by this suggestion, but Robert demurred. He recalled that Joliet was regularly an envoy of Talon, and the Intendant Talon was known for his close association with the Jesuits. He thought that Joliet might be trying to widen the breach between the priestly orders, and he asked whether the Jesuits hadn't already sent missionaries to the Pottawattamies.

"Yes," Joliet said, "they have."

"And mightn't they dislike the Sulpicians' intrusion? We're traveling to the Ohio," Robert said. "It would be folly to change our route. Father Queylus might think it an infidelity—"

Father Dollier broke in, haughtily: "La Salle, from now on we travel at my discretion, not yours. Father Galinée and I are going to the Upper Lakes, either with or without you, as you wish."

"And what is your wish, La Salle?" queried Joliet, smiling.

"I'm heading for the Ohio," said Robert.

On the last day of September the priests erected an altar of forked sticks and canoe paddles on the beach. Father Dollier said mass; the entire party knelt to worship. Then the altar was dismantled, the paddles were retrieved, and the canoes went scudding out on Lake Erie, leaving behind only Robert, Saget, and the Shawnee guide.

Watching, Robert felt that he had cast off a burden.

"Come, Peter," he said gaily. "Now we can do as we please."

They plunged afoot into the forest, their one canoe light on their shoulders. Reaching a navigable stream, they launched the slender craft and wound southward through a trackless solitude. Autumn flared with lovely color, then faded; it was winter, the canoe weaving through patches of ice which floated on a sluggish yellow river.

Robert looked at his imperfect maps, and at the river. Was this *la belle riviere*, the Ohio? The Shawnee said it was.

"And will the Ohio bear us to the Mississippi?"

The Shawnee said it would.

"But we're not seeking the Mississippi," Saget said. "Or perhaps we are! Yes, sir, I think it has always been the Mississippi—ever since you had those games of piquet with the ship's captain."

Robert smiled. "I'll not deny that I should like to see it."

With the advent of spring the yellow river flooded and leaped its banks. Once more they portaged—west across prairies to another river, which they followed until autumn. But the guide sulked now; he said he was worn out with the interminable wandering; he had aches and pains. One morning Robert woke to see Saget wrestling with the Shawnee, who wailed loudly.

Robert scrambled up. "Release him, Peter!"

"He was deserting, sir, crawling off without a beg-your-pardon!"

"Release him; he has earned it. Perhaps he's homesick."

"Homesick!" Saget ejaculated. "Perhaps I am too."

"We're going home," said Robert.

By stages, from stream to stream, they went toward home; but it was mid-July—they had been away a year —before they were again in the blockhouse with Nika and Jean Cavelier.

Robert asked his brother about Father Dollier and Father Galinée.

"After parting from you the priests passed through the Straits of Detroit," Jean said, "and wintered at the Sault Sainte Marie. Now they're back at the Seminary."

"What discoveries did they make?"

"None, and no conversions. The Jesuits rebuffed them."

"Sir," Nika said, "some Jesuits were here. They laugh at you for thinking you could find a new route to China."

"Yes, Robert, the Jesuits are ridiculing you—calling your seigniory *La Chine*," said Jean.

"La Chine? Well, it's not a bad name. Let them laugh, if they like," Robert said. "They may not always do so."

NEW FRIENDS, NEW PROSPECTS

V

In 1672 the King recalled Courcelle to France and appointed Louis de Buade, Count of Palluau and Frontenac, as Governor of Canada.

Poor Courcelle!—his vexations had finally been his undoing. Unable to keep peace with the Iroquois, estranged from Talon, he quit France, knowing that all his efforts in behalf of French sovereignty in North America were unappreciated. But Talon also had incurred the royal displeasure; Talon must resign as Intendant. This was, perhaps, Courcelle's one consolation.

Frontenac, the new governor, was a soldier and aristocrat whose diligent purpose would be to expand Canada into a great rich empire for his King. Surveying his position upon arrival, he saw that Talon had been promoting trips of exploration by teams of fur traders and missionaries—usually Jesuit missionaries. Indeed, one of Talon's last official acts had been to dispatch the Jesuit

priest Jacques Marquette with the fur-trading Louis
Joliet to explore for the elusive Mississippi; Marquette
and Joliet were well on their way before the new governor's ship had docked.

Frontenac was chagrined. He had no grudge against
the Jesuits, but in his opinion it was the duty of the
governor to retain complete control over all affairs
touching upon French supremacy in Canada—and the
Church must not overshadow the State! If possible he
would not involve himself in the priests' contest for
power, or accord any religious order preference above
others; and for his intimate associates he would have
about him only men—brave young men—who had
proved that their first devotion was to the King.

His discerning glance lighted upon the proprietor of
that oddly named place, La Chine; and he summoned
La Salle to Quebec for consultation.

Clad in his scarlet velvet, Robert was ushered in
before the Count de Frontenac. His immediate impres-
sion was of a vigorous, middle-aged man, handsome as a
sleek-plumaged hawk, with a hawk's flashing eye and
arrogant lift of the head. Frontenac was cordial, con-
fiding; yet behind his charm of manner was a vein of
uncompromising forcefulness. In a very few minutes
Robert had recognized that here was a friend, a future
ally—and more, a kindred spirit.

"I mean to build a fort on Lake Ontario," Frontenac
said. "To me such a fort seems absolutely necessary, to

inspire the Iroquois with a proper respect for us and put an end to these senseless wars."

"We shall never have peace without it," Robert said.

"I'm told that you have traversed much of that area."

"At one time or another, all of it," Robert said.

"The Bay of Quinté might be a good location."

"Catarqui would be better, sir."

"Catarqui?"

"An Iroquois settlement on the north shore, just beyond the Thousand Islands. A fort there could be defended." Robert paused. "You are aware that Governor Courcelle had this thought also?"

"Oh, yes! But Courcelle went at it from the wrong angle. Courcelle would no nothing without first getting the King's warrant—which was denied. I shall put up the fort, and get my warrant afterward."

"You know that some of the Canadian merchants are against it?"

"Yes, they say I lack troops, boats, weapons." Frontenac smiled. "Trifles! When the spring sowing is over, I'll require that our principal towns, Quebec, Montreal, Three Rivers, furnish me with a regiment of armed men, canoes, ammunition, and tools. And for you I have a special job."

"For me, sir?"

"I am advised that you speak the Indian languages."

"Yes, I do."

"I want you to go out among the tribes and bid the chiefs, the sachems, to a grand council—in July, shall we say?—at Catarqui, where my fort is to stand. I want to mollify the Indians, gain their allegiance and coopera-tion. Does this seem to you a reasonable idea, La Salle?"

"Yes, sir," Robert answered. "Reasonable and com-mendable."

"Well, you have three months—"

They were busy months, in which he made a full cir-cuit of the Iroquois towns. To persuade the chiefs and sachems of Governor Frontenac's good will was not easily done, for they had despised Courcelle and were dubious about his successor. Perhaps no one but La Salle could have smoothed their ruffled feathers. They knew La Salle as an extraordinary white man who, they said, behaved like an Indian, never flinching in the face of danger, with nerves of iron and tremendous physical endurance. In the past he had treated them with justice; now they believed him and promised to betake them-selves to Catarqui in July.

It was Frontenac's theory that pomp and ceremony should be displayed in this event. Starting from Quebec, June 3, with a few men and fewer canoes, he had halted at every village along the St. Lawrence to receive the homage due the King's representative, and to recruit workers in his cause. By the time he reached Catarqui he had four hundred men, one hundred and twenty canoes, and two large flatboats painted amazingly in patterns of bright blue and red. Alighting, he told La Salle that he had had a sort of conqueror's progress.

"Everywhere people flocked to honor me with banquets, prayers, *Te Deums*," he said. "You see I have quite an amount of baggage? Many of those boxes contain presents, trinkets and toys. To get them here we had literally to fight our way upstream, through your great rapids above La Chine. But Indians dote upon presents, and I had resolved to omit no detail of festivity. Well, I'm not the man to be shaken from a resolution, La Salle. And neither, I fancy, are you, eh? So let us pitch our tents, station sentinels, and kindle the fires— twenty of them!"

The council began at dawn, July 13, with a martial roll of drums and blast of bugles. Frontenac had spread the grass around his flag-decorated tent with a carpet made of sails from the flatboats. Attired in his most resplendent uniform, with his newly organized regiment behind him and La Salle standing at his side, he waited as the chiefs congregated.

"Children!" he said when all had drawn near. "I am *Onontio*, the Governor of Canada. How good it is to see you, where I have fires blazing for you to smoke by! You have done well, my children, to obey the command of your Father. Do not think that I have come for war. No! My mind is full of peace and tenderness. Take rest, children, and talk with me!"

Slowly, shyly, the Indians warmed to this appeal. The smiling countenance, the voice and words of the new Onontio were reassuring—and with him, evidently his friend, was the Sieur de La Salle, as always calm and courteous. The chiefs squatted on the canvas carpet, smoked the Onontio's excellent tobacco, and conversed with him through their interpreters; and meanwhile Frontenac's French engineers were tracing the lines for the foundation of a fort. In the evening there was a shower of gifts: guns for the tribesmen, packets of prunes and raisins for their wives, toys for their babies. At night the Indians retired to their temporary camp in the woods.

In the morning, as the council reassembled, Frontenac's axmen and carpenters applied themselves to building the fort, working so fast, so efficiently, that the Indians gaped in astonishment. Trenches were dug, logs hewed and laid; walls rose like magic. By dusk of July 17 the fort was almost finished.

Then Frontenac spoke formally again, saying that he was obliged to return to Quebec; the Iroquois must quietly disperse to their homes. A guard of soldiers would remain at Catarqui; later the Onontio would delegate someone to govern at the fort. He thanked them for their attendance, exhorted them to embrace Christianity and to listen only to men of character—"like the Sieur de La Salle," he said.

Stepping aboard the bigger of the flatboats, he added tactfully that the Onontio, though patient and loving, could be terrible if angered: "Beware how you offend him, my children!"

The flatboat was rowed downstream to La Chine, where Frontenac conferred with La Salle.

"The merchants will be furious with me," he said,

"and perhaps with you too. Yes, we'll have antagonized some people; but we have our fort on Lake Ontario—and you, La Salle, shall be suitably rewarded. You must go to France and inform the King of our accomplishment. I will petition His Majesty for your assignment as seignior of Fort Frontenac."

"But I have not hoped for any such reward!" Robert protested.

"Therefore you deserve it the more." Frontenac looked keenly at his young assistant. "Perhaps you have another kind of hope? Well, to be the overlord at Catarqui may pave the way for that—who knows? At any rate, I'll compose the petition which, at your convenience, you will carry to the King. It is my wish, La Salle. I think you will not be less obedient than my Indians, eh?"

"As a law-abiding subject I must obey the Governor's wishes," Robert said.

He sailed for France in the autumn of 1674, carrying not one petition, but two. He went to Paris and was most graciously received at court. Both his petitions were granted: in consideration of his explorations in Canada he was given a patent of nobility, with the rank of esquire; because of his services in the building of Fort Frontenac, he was made its seignior.

From Paris he went to Rouen, eager for a visit with his mother and all his family.

"Eight years you've been absent!" exclaimed Madame Cavelier, clasping him in her arms. "Eight years, Robert! You will notice many differences!"

Yes, there were differences. His mother was older, grayer; Paul had married and was the father of a little son named Colin; Marie's boy, Crevel, had shot up tall as Monsieur de Moranget's shoulder. But their affection and concern for Robert had not changed. And how they rejoiced at the honors just bestowed on him!

"So, Robert, you have a fort of your own?" said Paul.

He was stroking little Colin's blond hair, while Crevel hovered over him, listening admiringly. He smiled. "The fort is mine—if I can form a garrison there, plant a French colony, and domesticate the Indians around it."

Paul whistled. "What money have you?"

"My allowance—"

"Oh, that paltry thing! What else?"

"Well, I'll be in the fur trade. La Chine has been developed with the yield from my traps—though I've had to put every cent of it into the upkeep of the property. I have no cash."

"But this seigniory is more extensive than La Chine. Your fort should be fitted with cannon; your soldiers and laborers should have weapons, implements. Robert, you must borrow from me!"

"And from the de Morangets," Marie said.

"Yes," said Monsieur de Moranget, "we'll all invest in your career, Robert."

He reflected, and decided to borrow from them: "But I'll not forget that it's a loan. You will be paid in full!"

This time, leaving Rouen, he told his mother that he would visit her again. "Yes," he said, "I have a premonition."

"Do come!" said young Crevel. "I'll be a man then. La Salle and de Moranget! And Colin will be bigger. We'll both sail with you!"

The ship for Quebec was small and crowded. Robert spent his days on deck, staring over the rail at a measureless view of green water, his mind preoccupied with the new responsibilities he had assumed—and with that remote hope to which the seigniory of Fort Frontenac might pave the way.

"Why must I think of it so constantly?" he wondered. "Why must it nag me so?"

Behind him a violin wailed, feet shuffled. Glancing about, he saw six pretty girls dancing to the music—and a priest darting forward with upheld hand.

"Stop!" the priest cried. "Stop!"

The dancers stopped, abashed. The violinist rested his bow.

Robert wheeled upon the priest. "What is the meaning of this interference? Of course, they may dance. On with the tune, fiddler. And as for you, sir, out of the way or you'll be trampled."

The music rose in gay crescendo; the girls smiled and swung their partners.

"You are the Sieur de La Salle?" said the priest.

"Yes. And you?"

"I am Louis Hennepin. I do not like merrymaking. It is unseemly."

Robert looked with amusement at the plump little man in the gray hood and gown of a Recollet friar. "What do you like, sir?"

"Prayers, meditations—"

"Young people can't be eternally praying, meditating!"

Louis Hennepin pursed his lips. "A sincere Christian might not voice such sentiments."

"Indeed?" Robert laughed. "I challenge you to say I'm not a sincere Christian."

"It is rumored that you once were on the verge of dedicating your life to religion."

"And you are at liberty to think that my hot temper ruled me out. But do you delight in nothing worldly, nothing at all?"

"Frankly, yes." Hennepin inclined his cowled head. "Yes, I confess it as a sin that I dearly love to hear the anecdotes of sailors. I've just been in Calais, where many sea captains come. I would actually hide behind the tavern doors to listen to tales of their cruises. The tobacco fumes sickened me; my brain reeled; my limbs were cramped—yet it seemed I couldn't tear myself away. Why, I've passed whole days and nights in this entertainment! I have these twin zeals, to save souls and to travel abroad. Now I am going to Canada."

"As a missionary?"

"A missionary—and an explorer. In Canada exploring

parties must always have priests; it is the edict of our noble King. I believe, sir, that you are a renowned explorer."

"Renowned? Oh, no!"

"I would be a good man for such undertakings. Talented, versatile. Why, I can do anything, everything—"

As the little priest prattled on about himself, his virtues, peculiarities, and harmless vanities, Robert gazed out to sea.

"A renowned explorer?" he thought. "Not very. Not yet."

THE GRAND ENTERPRISE

VI

L A SALLE worked quickly and conscientiously at Catarqui. Within two years he had fulfilled every condition of the King's grant and squared his debts to the Rouen relatives.

His seigniory was now as fine as any in Canada. The large stone fort, which replaced the original wooden structure, had nine brass cannon on the walls and was occupied by a company of uniformed soldiers, two officers, and a surgeon. Laborers, masons, and carpenters were housed inside the palisade; and, outside, two villages had sprung up, one of Iroquois families, the other of French families who had come from Montreal with their children, their cattle, fowls, and pigs. More than a hundred acres of land had been planted in crops; four boats flying La Salle's colors plied the lake; and at the river piers were dozens of canoes, ready for instant use, with skilled men to handle them. As for the fur trade, it flourished and was the envy of all the district.

If he had wished only for prosperity, this existence would have brought him contentment—instead, he chafed at the restraints it imposed. He could not believe that, in Jean's phrase, he had been born a rover; but neither could he believe that his destiny was to be a feudal lord, a gentleman farmer. Often he reflected that, while he lived so snugly here, other men were having adventures which should be his.

Then an astounding report reached him. On June 17, 1673, the Jesuit priest Marquette, with Louis Joliet, had rediscovered the Mississippi River!

Could the report be true? La Salle went to Quebec for confirmation of it.

Yes, the facts were known. Through the straits of Michilimackinac, along Lake Michigan's northern shores, to the Menominee River, to Green Bay, the Fox River, across Lake Winnebago, down the Wisconsin River, Marquette and Joliet had pressed—and out upon the Father of Waters. For a month the Mississippi had borne their canoe southward to the influx of the Arkansas River, where they had turned back. By the last of September they were again at Green Bay, having paddled more than twenty-five hundred miles and proved conclusively that this greatest of rivers must have its mouth at the Gulf of Mexico.

Marquette's achievement was roundly applauded in

Canada; for he was loved and revered there as a devout and saintly man, the very model of Christian integrity. But almost before the echoes of that applause faded came a second report.

Marquette was dead. From Green Bay he had started for the Illinois River to found a mission. His strength was exhausted, his health frail. In a thatched mud hut on the river bank, surrounded by sorrowing Indian converts, the valiant priest had died.

In Quebec, La Salle talked of Marquette with Governor Frontenac.

"I am puzzled, sir, as to why Marquette didn't complete his exploration. He went so far—and why not farther? According to Joliet, the Indians on the Arkansas are very fierce. Couldn't Marquette have tamed them? And does it suffice merely to look at the Mississippi and write of it in a journal? No, all the adjacent land should have been claimed as the property of France—claimed and fortified!"

Frontenac smiled. "You forget that Marquette was a missionary, not a colonizer. I suppose he did as much as Talon had expected of him."

"And you, as governor, are entirely pleased with the results?"

"Perhaps not entirely, La Salle."

"Nor am I. In Marquette's place I would have persevered; I would have seen with my own eyes the Mississippi's confluence with the Gulf. I would have gained for France a permanent addition of territory too vast and wonderful to be imagined!"

"That is what you've always had in mind, isn't it?" Frontenac said. "From your first day in America?"

"And even before," La Salle answered simply. "I cannot tell you, sir, how I feel about the Mississippi. You couldn't understand; no one could—but I would have forfeited half my life to have come upon it as Marquette did!"

Frontenac thoughtfully tapped his fingers on the table. "You may yet have the chance. Marquette's was only a partial success. You may yet be the hero of the Mississippi. Let us put our heads together, Robert. Let us plan a grand enterprise, eh?"

During the spring of 1677 the two friends frequently had their heads together. Between them they evolved a plan for French expansion in America which would surely surpass anything previously considered.

It was Frontenac's desire that these conferences be private.

"I have made many enemies in Canada, La Salle," he said—and enumerated them: "The merchants who never have been reconciled to the building of our Lake Ontario fort; the Jesuits who think that I curtail their priestly endeavors; the Sulpicians who feel that I'm not at heart a religious man, myself." He grinned wryly. "Then there are other plaintive folk who see me as a ruthless executive riding roughshod to attain my own ends. All such persons murmur in their beards that I must one day suffer for my brashness. Yes, and you also!"

"I?" La Salle said.

"You have cast your lot with mine. You're included in the prejudice against me!"

"But what you've done is for the good of the people."

"Ah, they haven't the intelligence to realize that! So we'll not harry them with knowledge of our new project, eh?"

"Very well," La Salle said, "though I don't fear their murmurings, or ever think of them."

Indeed, he thought of nothing now except his conquest of the Mississippi, the forming of his party. Frontenac said that, for a thing so important, the King's patronage must be secured.

"You'll have to go to Paris with a written memorial to be read by the King and his ministers."

La Salle carefully penned the "memorial," a lengthy manuscript in which he recited his past explorations; stated his hopes for this one; and painted a glowing picture of the Mississippi valley, its resources and potential treasure—the advisability of seizing and developing it before other nations should intervene. England, for instance, was eying this fertile land; England encroached upon French possessions everywhere. And in Mexico were the avaricious Spaniards, bent upon controlling all the North American continent.

The main plea of the memorial was for the privilege of making a tour in the King's name, with the right to erect two forts at strategic positions. La Salle himself would reckon with the expense, from his own purse and the income from his fur trade at Catarqui. The King would have no obligation, no investment but his royal approbation. Great hardship would be incurred by any person who descended the titanic river—

"But these will only animate the Sieur de La Salle the more!"

Frontenac scanned the finished document and pronounced it excellent: "You've written with enthusiasm, zest, eloquence. Take it to Colbert, the King's minister of finance. Colbert is a man of lofty vision. I think he will be much moved."

La Salle embarked for France that autumn; and in the spring Louis XIV issued a patent conceding all that had been implored of him, and more. On a parchment scroll, countersigned by Colbert, stamped with the imperial seal and splashed with yellow wax, Louis declared that La Salle was empowered to explore and to construct forts wherever necessary.

The King addressed La Salle flatteringly, even fondly, as his "dear Robert Cavelier," his "well-beloved." But he had attached one qualifying clause:

The grand enterprise must be completed within five years.

"Five years? I can do it!" thought La Salle.

He was several months in France. At his mother's house in Rouen he saw his relatives.

"You had a premonition!" exclaimed his nephew Crevel. "And now can I go to America with you?"

"No, Crevel. Not yet. Wait just a bit more."

"But you will take me—*sometime?* And Colin too?"

"Yes, yes." La Salle laughed. "How obstinate you are, Crevel. As Nurse Elise once said—a donkey!"

One day in the Rouen streets he saw Father Guiscard. Feeble and tremulous, the old priest embraced him.

"They tell me, Robert, that you're a famous man in Canada—and still an honest man. I pray for you always."

"Thank you, Father Guiscard," he said humbly. "Your prayers will sustain me."

Back in Paris, he bought baggage and ammunition, rigging, cordage, and an anchor for the boat he would build to sail the western rivers. Frontenac had given him letters of introduction to persons prominent at court; through one such acquaintance of Frontenac, he met Henry de Tonty—a circumstance for which he would ever afterward be glad.

La Salle was dining at the palace of the Prince de Conti when he encountered the swarthy-skinned young Italian and observed his flashing smile, his compact, agile figure, and the gloved hand below his right coat sleeve.

"You are a soldier, Monsieur de Tonty?"

"I *was* a soldier, sir, in the Sicilian wars. This glove," Tonty said, "hides a metal makeshift for the thing of flesh and bone which was blown off by a grenade in Sicily. The accident endowed me with a nickname, Tonty of the Iron Hand, and robbed me of my profession. I'm looking now for work of another sort."

"Ah?"

"To be candid, sir," Tonty said, "the Prince has told me of your proposed exploration, and that you are hiring recruits in Paris."

"Yes, I've rounded up thirty men here. In Canada I'll get more."

"Perhaps you want a lieutenant—a fellow tough as leather, impervious to bullets, and guaranteeing to do more with one paw than most fellows can do with two. If so, I am at your service."

"We can at least talk about it."

Before the evening was over, La Salle was discussing plans with Henry de Tonty, his new lieutenant. The party, he said, would start from Catarqui in relays of ten or fifteen, in small boats and by diverse routes, for the Niagara River, where all would muster on the plateau above the cataract to build a large vessel—the *Griffin*.

"The *Griffin*?" Tonty repeated. "You have a name for your vessel?"

"Yes, a name which compliments my patron, Governor Frontenac."

"But what is a griffin, sir?"

"A griffin, Tonty, is the fabulous creature, half eagle, half lion, on the Frontenac coat of arms."

Aboard their vessel the party would sail for Green Bay, La Salle said; and though winter was coming, the cold weather would not deter him. In Canada the weather was usually inclement; winter seemed to run through most of the calendar.

"And we'll be going toward the equator, a balmier climate," Tonty said.

La Salle smiled. "Not for many weeks and miles! Probably you have as yet no conception of the yawning distances in America; it's a thing Europeans can seldom envisage. We're going to the lower Mississippi; before we get there, we'll be exposed to the extremes of temperature, paralyzing cold, wilting heat—and worse discomforts. But, now that I have the King's commission, I am like a race horse, Tonty, straining at the barrier."

"Nothing could stop you, eh?"

"Nothing."

"The members of your party," Tonty said. "Can you depend on them?"

"Oh, I think so. Some I've known for years, as well as I know myself: Peter Saget, the Shawnee Nika, La Forest from Catarqui, Louis Hennepin, who preaches at my seigniory church—"

"Hennepin? A priest?"

"Yes, a Recollet friar, and in his own words a veritable globe-trotter. No explorer fares forth without a clergyman. I'll test Father Hennepin's abilities."

"But the others?" Tonty said. "Those from Paris, are they trustworthy?"

La Salle shrugged. "Why wouldn't they be? Yes, I trust them, and I'm sailing soon from La Rochelle. Is that convenient for you?"

"The sooner, the better," said Tonty.

THE NORTHERN WINTER

VII

In November, 1678, the explorers left Fort Frontenac by their several routes. In January they mustered at the rendezvous above Niagara Falls—and not a man of them but had stories to tell of obstacles on the way.

Some had been misled by Indians who took their gifts of beads and knives, cloth and needles, and then grew sullen and menacing. Some had been detained by illness in weather never more raw and frosty. One of the supply boats had been wrecked, its precious cargo sinking to the bottom of the St. Lawrence, the passengers saving themselves only by stout feats of swimming in icebound water.

La Salle simply closed his ears to such recountings. He believed that he could placate the Indians, that the sick would get well. Undaunted, he sent fifteen men on to Michilimackinac, where they were to trade for furs; with those who remained, he began work on the *Griffin*.

Tools and materials were hauled up the snow-clad steeps to the plateau; trees were hewed and planed into timbers. La Salle himself laid the *Griffin's* keel and drove the first bolt into her hull.

Then he called Tonty to him.

"We must have more gear, ammunition, and food," he said. "I'm going back to Fort Frontenac. You stay, to supervise the shipbuilding."

"You can't go alone," Tonty said.

"I'll take Saget and Nika."

"And the priest? He can be spared."

"Father Hennepin? You have no love for him, have you, Tonty?"

"Hennepin is an officious little braggart—and he has no love for me. However," Tonty said, "it's not the moment to argue that. You know that the streams are too clogged with ice for canoes to be floated?"

"I'll get a sled from the Indians and a dog to pull it. We'll strap a bag of corn on the sled and walk behind it."

"Two hundred and fifty miles?" Tonty grimaced. "A long walk."

"Yes. Therefore we must start!"

La Salle could never afterward describe that march from the Niagara to Catarqui. His impressions of it were hazy, blurred—the days, weeks, months of plodding from dawn to dark through winter-white country; the nights of fitful sleep in forest pockets, where wild animals prowled and wild winds shrieked in the treetops. The three marchers were always cold, often hungry, occasionally threatened by starvation. But La Salle's unyielding will held him to the path, and the unquestioning devotion of Saget and Nika held them to their stern master.

It was spring before they passed through the gate of Fort Frontenac's palisade, and La Salle was still resolute. The Abbé Cavelier hurried from Montreal to see him.

"You're gaunt as a ghost, Robert," Jean said. "You must rest."

"I must get supplies to the Niagara! Don't lecture me, Jean. Have some canoes readied."

But unexpected complications loomed suddenly. Governor Frontenac came from Quebec to report that the Jesuits were circulating scandalous rumors about the Sieur de La Salle, labeling him as a dolt, a harebrained idiot—a scoundrel:

"They say you've borrowed money you'll never repay."

La Salle was indignant. Yes, he had borrowed money—

"I had to! The costs of my equipment were exorbitant; the Canadian merchants overcharged me for every purchase."

"And can you clear yourself of the indebtedness?"

"Not now. Later I will—to the penny!"

"Later? I'm afraid," Frontenac said, "your creditors won't wait. The Jesuits have told them to invoke the law."

"The Jesuits?"

"They are suing for your property at La Chine, as payment."

"Well, let them have La Chine!" La Salle cried furiously.

"They may then sue for your seigniory here."

"But why should the Jesuits be in league with the merchants against me? This is petty persecution—and not the first instance."

"The Jesuits are jealous of you," Frontenac said. "Your men are on the Niagara; you have a foothold at a point which is the key to the whole of the five Great Lakes, an area they have regarded as theirs exclusively."

"I'm not infringing on their rights to preach, to convert, to spread the Christian doctrine. I don't understand the situation! But I can't believe that the Church is behind it, for I have lived by the Church and know it to be infallible."

Frontenac nodded.

"I can't believe the Jesuit order is composed entirely of jealous scandalmongers."

"No."

"Well, then?"

Frontenac looked very sober. "La Salle, in Asia, Africa, and South America the Jesuits have had free rein as missionaries and, more than that, as dictators of government; in Paraguay they have been unhampered, doing just as they wished. You say the Church is infallible, and I agree. You say the Jesuits must be mostly good; again I agree. But it would seem that their successes in other countries have turned the heads of some members of the order—perhaps not all. The stark fact is, the Jesuits in North America are greedy for power; their purpose has been to make Canada one big mission, ruled by themselves."

Frontenac paused. "It may be that former representatives of the King have bowed to them. *I* have not. I never will. *My* purpose is to maintain Canada as an imperial possession. I administer the government for the State, rather than for any religious order. The offense is one for which the Jesuits cannot forgive me, and because of my policies you, as my friend, are persecuted."

La Salle was silent, remembering what Talon had said to him long ago—that priests are but men, not angels; ambitious, some of them—and Courcelle's tired voice insinuating that ambition is a defect shared by all human beings. And earlier there had been Father Guiscard's warning. . . . Was this his defect too? Was his ambition merely selfishness?

"I cannot think so. . . . I cannot think so!"

He went to Quebec, where, with Frontenac's help, he raised cash enough to reimburse the most clamorous of his creditors.

"And now go on to Niagara and the Mississippi," Frontenac said. "I'll do everything possible in your interests here."

"I have men at Michilimackinac and Green Bay collecting furs. I'll send you the furs."

"Good! Turned into money, they can assure your ownership of the Catarqui seigniory."

In August he rejoined his party. As his canoe entered the Niagara River, he saw a fine large vessel anchored below the plateau.

It was the *Griffin*—complete even to her flaunting banner and the five brass cannon peeping from her portholes!

He sprang ashore and rushed to congratulate Tonty.

"The boat is beautiful!" he exclaimed. "A beautiful symbol of what we will accomplish!"

Tonty smiled ruefully. "I had my troubles with her. The men grumbled and shirked—I shouted myself hoarse keeping them at the job! The Indians have been an infernal nuisance; it seems you're the only white man in Canada they'll listen to. Once they set fire to the *Griffin*, as she was on the stocks; once a drunken Seneca went at our blacksmith with a sledge hammer and nearly brained him."

La Salle nodded, saying nothing of his own troubles. Indeed, the sight of the splendid boat had erased them from his thoughts.

"Father Hennepin was a nuisance too," Tonty continued. "Globe-trotter? He just patters around to Indian camps, or dawdles, writing yarns in his journal about the customs of the natives. If I may be so bold, sir, the little fussbudget is a misfit in this expedition. He's conceited, and gossipy as an old woman—"

"Yes, I know that Hennepin can be annoying. But never mind, Tonty; I've brought two other Recollets from Fort Frontenac—"

"More priests!"

"Good ones," La Salle said soothingly. "Father Zenobe Membré and Father Gabriel Ribourde. With them as examples, Father Hennepin may improve."

Tonty's smile flashed. "Plenty of room for improvement, sir!"

When the canoes were unpacked, La Salle handed Saget a doeskin-wrapped bundle and a heavy bronze box.

"Guard these for me."

"Yes, sir." Saget's black eyes snapped inquisitively. "What's in them?"

"In the bundle, my scarlet cloak. I'll wear it at Michilimackinac."

"Ah, that gala cloak, that useful cloak! And in the box?"

"A leaden plate engraved with the King's arms. I'll plant it in the earth at the mouth of the Mississippi."

Saget put the box under his jacket. "It will be guarded with my very life!"

On August 7 a breeze blew fresh and strong; the sheets of the *Griffin* filled, and La Salle's party went aboard. Prayers were intoned and *Te Deums* chanted. The anchor was upheaved; with a burst of cannon fire the graceful vessel glided forth into Lake Erie—the first sailboat ever to navigate those waters. Southwest to the

Straits of Detroit, across Lake St. Clair, angling north through the St. Clair River and into Lake Huron, the *Griffin* majestically made her way, outriding a series of summer storms, sailing on toward the woody island of Michilimackinac.

When La Salle glimpsed the furrowed blue surface of Lake Michigan opening before him, he donned his velvet cloak. A few hours more and he could see the roofs of the town on St. Ignace, then throngs of people swarming to welcome the oncoming vessel. The *Griffin's* guns thundered a salute; the townsfolk gestured an answering greeting. Alighting, the explorers paraded to the Michilimackinac chapel, where they heard mass and knelt to thank God for His protection of them during this initial stage of their journey. All that day and the next the *Griffin* was the object of admiring comment.

But La Salle did not see any of the fifteen men who had started in advance to trade for furs in this rich fur country, and he was disturbed. Not for an instant had he forgotten his creditors in Quebec. Without the valuable pelts from Michilimackinac to compensate them, the querulous merchants might snatch at the seigniory at Catarqui. Without the seigniory, he would have no finances to draw upon; he could not carry forward his grand enterprise!

Trying to be optimistic, he said to Tonty that perhaps the fifteen men, all of them, were at Green Bay.

"Or they may have deserted," suggested Tonty bluntly. "Nika has talked with the Huron and Ottawa

Indians of St. Ignace. They say some white traders were there recently, laden with beaver and otter skins, and going to the Falls of Sainte Marie. I think those were our men. Let me go and fetch the filthy rascals, and their plunder too. You find out what's happening at Green Bay. I'll overtake you shortly."

When Tonty had started for Sainte Marie, La Salle sailed the *Griffin* to Green Bay, where he was heartened to find six of the advance group and an accumulation of fine furs.

"Get the furs baled and stacked," he said to Saget. "I'm sending them on the *Griffin* to an agent of Governor Frontenac at Niagara."

Saget hesitated. "Gales are predicted—"

"The *Griffin* is a sturdy craft."

"And pretty as a swan! Too bad to risk her—"

"Life is made up of risks," La Salle said irritably. "Are you such a fool as not to know it?"

"Oh, no, sir," said Saget. "I know it."

On September 18, with one farewell booming of cannon, the *Griffin* set out from Green Bay. From the shore La Salle watched as her white canvas wings swept over the horizon's rim. Wind whistled shrilly in the trees' sere branches; gray clouds mantled the sky. Unaccountably sad, he sighed—and heard his sigh echoed behind him. He wheeled, and saw Saget.

"Peter! Must you always be at my elbow?"

"Always, sir," Saget said. "My duty, ever since that day in Rouen. I had nipped an apple—"

"From the fruit peddler's cart. Yes, yes."

"One tiny wrinkled apple—"

"A dull and stupid tale. Be quiet!"

After a quiet interval Saget said: "It's like the time on the Lake Erie beach, when Father Dollier and Father Galinée paddled off."

"It's not at all like that. I had no one then but you and an incompetent guide. I have fourteen men now, three friars, four large canoes, provisions of every sort. We were going to the Ohio then, and uncertain of finding it; we're going now to the Mississippi, which I'll find or die in the attempt! And we haven't seen the last of the *Griffin*—"

"No?"

"Of course not! My command to the pilot was to put back from Niagara to the spot where the St. Joseph River merges with Lake Michigan. The pilot will obey. We start tomorrow for the St. Joseph."

"Tomorrow? But what of Tonty?"

"I'll leave messages here for Tonty. He will overtake us."

The wind sharpened, and La Salle shivered. It was autumn; winter was in the offing—and far out on the steel-blue lake, ever farther, went the gallant *Griffin*.

VIII

From Green Bay the four canoes skirted Lake Michigan's west coast toward the curved southern shore line and the inlet of the St. Joseph, which the Indians had named the River of the Miamis.

The passage was not an easy one. Those predicted gales had blown fiercely. The canoes, freighted with such unwieldy articles as a blacksmith's forge, carpenters' tools, and chests of ammunition, had wallowed and floundered in the churning water. The men were wet, cramped, hungry—and morose, for they had thought to make this trip on the commodious *Griffin*. Rather silently, in a pelting rain, the party landed, and climbed the bluff above the river.

"We'll build a fort and stay here until Tonty comes —and the *Griffin*," La Salle said.

The men protested vehemently. They wanted to travel, not to build; they wanted to winter in the south, not on this wind-wracked eminence. But La Salle repeated staunchly that he would have a fort; if necessary he would build it with his own hands; if necessary, remain in it alone.

"I think that Saget, Nika, and our good priests will not forsake me. You others may stay or go, as you prefer."

Grudgingly they preferred to stay. The fort was begun, took shape, at length was finished and called Fort Miami. Then La Salle laid the foundations of a chapel in which mass could be said daily, with special services on Sundays.

Tonty came in late November. With him were two of the scapegraces he had intercepted at Sainte Marie and ten new recruits from St. Ignace. Behind their pirogues they towed a raft on which were the frozen carcasses of two stags Tonty had shot.

La Salle was grateful for the stags. He said the men would relish some meals of savory venison—game had been remarkably scarce; they were eking out their slim rations with nuts and dried wild berries. As the meat was being thawed and cooked, he told Tonty of his experiences in the weeks elapsed since their parting.

He was pleased with the work done on the fort and chapel; the Recollets, he said, had been cheerful, though Father Ribourde was almost too old and Father Hennepin too boastful to be of much assistance. Of course, Hennepin did have intelligence and zeal; as leader of a party of his own, he might be very proficient—

"But I cannot let him lead this one, Tonty."

"No," Tonty said, smiling. "And Father Membré?"

"He is the flower of the flock. Membré has won the affection of us all. As for the men, they seem to lack spirit."

"Do they?" Tonty thought about this, and said that at Michilimackinac the scurrilous falsehoods of the Jesuits might have penetrated to the men, and been believed by them. "The Jesuits were there, you know; they mingled with our fellows—and they're tricky."

"The men would not believe that I'm a dolt, a scoundrel."

"Perhaps not—but many of them are dolts and scoundrels themselves, eager to tar others with the same feather. Well, we must keep an eye on them, discipline them. And what tidings of the *Griffin*, sir?"

"None," La Salle said grimly. "I've looked for her day and night."

"She may be lost."

Lost? The *Griffin*, the symbol of achievement? "No, Tonty! No!"

"But can you afford to wait here indefinitely?"

"No," La Salle said. "I'll post La Forest in Fort Miami, with a few men to tend the boat when she arrives —as she must and will! The rest of us will go on to the Illinois and the Mississippi."

Tonty nodded. "It's snowing. A year ago, in my ignorance, I'd have thought we couldn't face such a blizzard. Today I snap my thumb at blizzards! So let us be off."

At the upper end of the St. Joseph was a five-mile portage which La Salle wished to traverse and put behind him. The narrow, twisting path, regularly used by Indians, connected the St. Joseph with the Kankakee and had peculiar significance because it marked a natural watershed. For months the explorers had paddled strenuously against the current in all the northern streams. Now they would have the current with them to speed their progress.

Snow fell thickly as they maneuvered through the portage, single-file, slowly, carrying the heavy canoes. Wherever they paused, whether to eat or sleep, or to relax aching muscles, La Salle carved crosses into the tree trunks. Who knew, he said, but that they might come this way again?

"This obscure little lane may someday be a link in a great chain of travel between Canada, French colonies in the continent's interior, and the Gulf of Mexico."

The Kankakee River took them through weedy, ice-encrusted marshes with views of dreary prairies from which the Indians, even the birds and beasts, had migrated for the winter season. The Illinois was faster-flowing, the surrounding land hillier. Presently they saw an enormous pillar of stone overhanging the river.

"Starved Rock," La Salle said. "The Indians speak of it."

He would remember that towering height, the sheer cliff, the tree-tufted summit. A fort at the top of Starved Rock would be impregnable!

Beyond, on the north shore of the Illinois, was a large Indian village, plainly discernible from the canoes, but so soundless, so static, that it seemed at first glance to have the quality of a mirage. Father Membré thought this must be La Vantum, the city of the Kaskaskias, who were an Illinois tribe.

"We'll have a look at it," La Salle said.

They disembarked and walked up through neatly plotted streets, all silent and empty. Father Hennepin counted the dwellings and noted the number in his journal: four hundred and sixty, all vacant, doors ajar, hearths blackened with cold ashes.

"Marquette wrote of La Vantum," Father Membré said. "He was here in 1675; he had a church; he preached and converted most of the five thousand inhabitants. Good Marquette! He was praying for another such triumph of godliness when he made his last mission."

Father Hennepin said that La Vantum must have grown since Marquette's visit: "The population now would probably exceed seven thousand, or eight."

"But why the mystery?" Tonty asked. "Where are the people?"

"They have gone to some southern hunting ground," Nika said. "Like the Indians of the Kankakee marshes, they chase the deer and buffalo."

In the rear of the streets were brown cornfields and huts in which baskets of corn had been stored. La Salle said that La Vantum had harvested a fair grain crop.

"I'll take a small amount. Saget, scoop out thirty-five bushels; measure accurately, and I'll somehow contrive to pay the Kaskaskias for it. We are in sore need of bread."

As Saget scooped the corn from the spilling baskets, he muttered that he would not fancy lingering here.

"La Vantum? A city of ghosts," he said.

They lingered only briefly, then went down the Illinois. On New Year's Day, January 1, 1680, they landed in a cove for religious worship. Four days later they were at the widening of the river known as Lake Peoria, and La Salle stepped ashore to reconnoiter.

Soon he haled in the party. He had seen a cluster of wigwams, occupied by Indians who seemed friendly.

"They're Kaskaskias, a branch of the tribe from La Vantum. I gave them tobacco and hatchets in exchange for the grain from their stores in the big town. I told them I would camp on Lake Peoria for a few weeks."

During those weeks La Salle was frequently entertained in the clustered wigwams. He dined with the Kaskaskias; witnessed their dances; smoked their peace pipe, the calumet, with its bowl of finely polished red stone, its yard-long stem of cane decorated lavishly with rainbow-dyed feathers, dangling silver coins, and strands of human hair. He conversed with them, and they were invariably well-mannered. Yet he had the feeling that this was pretense, that actually, secretly, they were hostile to him.

Then, through Nika, he learned that his surmise was correct.

Monso, a Miami medicine man, had appeared on Lake Peoria. Monso, with five painted Miami chieftains, came in pirogues filled with kettles, axes, knives. Monso's pirogues were moored very inconspicuously in a tangle of willows; at night, when the white men had retired to their separate camp, Monso crept to the wigwams to dispense his presents and whisper an alarm.

The Iroquois, Monso said, were girding for warfare; the Iroquois, the dread Five Nations, would swoop upon and annihilate all the Indians in the Illinois valley:

"They are bad, the Iroquois; they fight like furies, rending limb from limb. The white strangers among you are bad, and La Salle is the most evil of them. La Salle is a spy of the Iroquois, a devil in the guise of man. Cast him out, cast him out—"

La Salle was appalled. "Is this information reliable, Nika?"

"It is. I have seen Monso, heard him. I think *he* is the spy. Someone has sent him to the Kaskaskias—someone who would prevent your discovery of the Mississippi. It may be that the Iroquois are girding to strike, I cannot tell. But Monso's pretty baubles, his bribes, his warnings, these have been furnished by someone else, not by the Five Nations."

"The Jesuits again, I'll wager!" said Tonty. "The Jesuits, blast them, are inciting Monso!"

La Salle frowned. "Perhaps not. We must not jump to conclusions."

"Why not?" Tonty cried. "Why be so charitable when we have evidence?"

"We have no evidence, just indications. Let Nika tell us everything he knows."

"I know only that Monso should be proved wrong," said Nika, "or he will do us great mischief."

La Salle went immediately and boldly to the wigwams; he denounced Monso, scoffed at his tales as absurd and false. But the mischief had been done: the Kaskaskias had discarded their mask of friendliness; they shunned him.

"We'll never have any satisfactory dealings with them now," Tonty said. "We'd best withdraw and put up a fort, in which we can defend ourselves in case of attack. And whatever else we may attribute to Monso, he has scared the wits out of our Frenchmen. Five have deserted already—and I think there'll be more."

On a hill between two ravines La Salle constructed his fort, enclosing its four blockhouses with a palisade and digging a trench around its oblong sides.

Fort Crêvecœur, he called it, Fort of the Broken Heart, for indeed it seemed the refuge of one constantly plagued by heartbreaking misfortunes.

In Crêvecœur he began to build a second boat, smaller than the first, designed for river transportation.

The work went falteringly—and, for La Salle, sorrowfully. Though the Indians had not interfered, his own men had an air of moodiness and furtive apprehension. He felt weary and distraught; and every plank that was cut, every nail driven, reminded him of the *Griffin*. . . .

Where was the *Griffin* now? And what of Frontenac, what of the creditors who coveted the seigniory at Catarqui?

One night he could not sleep. Flinging a coat about him, he started from his quarters diagonally across the oblong enclosure toward the corner blockhouse in which Tonty had his room. Darkness shrouded the outer world; no moon shone, no stars; but in Tonty's window a candle beamed. La Salle walked fast, boot heels clicking on the frozen ground.

Suddenly a gun exploded, a bullet whizzed; the loose sleeve of La Salle's coat was clipped into shreds.

At the same instant Tonty's door was jerked open and from the threshold came Tonty's voice:

"Run! In here!"

La Salle ran, darting into the candlelit room. Tonty slammed the door and leaned against it.

"Indians!" La Salle panted, and shook his torn sleeve. "They almost got me."

"Indians? Perhaps not." Tonty bolted the door. "Sit down."

La Salle sank onto a stool. "Why do you say that? Somebody shot at me, shot to kill—"

"It may not have been an Indian."

"But who else?"

"One of the men."

La Salle stared. "Oh, no! *Oh, no!*"

"You think not?" Tonty nodded, his eyes glinting with anger. "I think most of them are cowards, wretches, not worth the powder and ball to blow them to perdition!"

"You judge them too harshly, Tonty."

"And you, too leniently." Tonty sat down. "What, really, do you know about your men? What did you know of me, when you hired me there in Paris? Next to nothing! You took me as your lieutenant without even asking for a reference. I might have been the biggest mountebank in Christendom—you made no inquiries! With few exceptions you've hired all your party just as recklessly. Of course, I see the predicament: you had to get men for your venture; and men who want such employment are mostly homeless waifs, derelicts. Still, you should have been more discriminating!"

La Salle flushed. "I suppose the ten recruits you got at Michilimackinac are better stuff, eh?"

"Yes, they are. At least none of them has deserted."

"Tonty, do you presume to chide me? To scold me?"

"Yes, I do."

"But—how dare you!"

"Sir," Tonty said earnestly, "I think you're the bravest man I've ever known. The bravest—but dangerously idealistic. Because you are honorable yourself, you never probe into the character of others. The fault is serious; it could be fatal in a business like this. Your intentions are above reproach; your sense of obligation is inflexible; it would never occur to you that other men might be duped, hoodwinked, corrupted—or simply frightened. I tell you, we're companioned by rogues!"

"I don't believe you!" La Salle was irate. "And if it is so, if you have this uncanny perception, this insight, why didn't you tell me in Paris, in Quebec?"

"Would you have believed me then? No," Tonty said. "And in Paris, in Quebec, the men had not yet been demoralized by fear, hunger, loneliness. Not everybody can withstand months and years of privation—a fact you blindly disregard."

La Salle got to his feet. "Tonty, I'm going back to Canada."

"What!"

"I came tonight to tell you that. I must talk with Frontenac, about the *Griffin*, my seigniory, my creditors. The suspense is too much for me. You say our men are rogues; I say they're decent, loyal fellows who need more food, clothing, equipment. In Canada I'll get these things for them."

"Canada is more than a thousand miles away."

"Yes, it is. I won't return until the summer."

Tonty rose, walked to the window, looked out.

"You persist in thinking a Frenchman fired that shot?"

"I do," Tonty said. "I wish I didn't! Well, sir, you're going, and you want me to hold on here through the winter and spring? I will. But I urge that you take Saget and Nika with you; Hunaut and La Violette too. They are the pick of our sorry lot."

"Nika, Hunaut, La Violette? Yes." La Salle nodded. "Not Saget—he's ailing; he coughs."

"The priests?"

"I've considered the priests. You once said Hennepin is a misfit—and he is, I grant it. I've decided to send Hennepin with two men, any two he selects, to explore the tributaries of the Illinois."

"As captain of his own party?" Tonty smiled. "The little fussbudget will be very happy—and maybe even famous, eh?"

"Quite possibly," La Salle said. "Membré and Ribourde will stay on at Crêvecœur."

As he went out into the night, he saw a figure crouched beneath Tonty's window.

"Saget?"

"Yes, sir? Good evening, sir."

"Eavesdropping!"

"Not at all. I heard a gun—"

"You are incorrigible, Peter."

"Yes, sir. And I cough. But I'm no more ailing today than a week ago. I'll not cough worse in Canada than in this drafty fort."

"Oh, very well," La Salle said, sighing.

The five men left Crêvecœur on the first day of March; sixty-five days later they were at Fort Frontenac. If La Salle's previous journey from Niagara to Catarqui had been long, this one was four times longer, a hundred times more grueling.

And the situation in Canada was not encouraging.

The *Griffin* had never made port, never been sighted. Beautiful and graceful as a white swan, the *Griffin* must surely have glided into oblivion in the tempestuous wastes of Lake Michigan.

Governor Frontenac, though as always sympathetic, was coping with knotty personal problems. The King had appointed a new Intendant at Quebec.

"His name is Duschenau, and I loathe him," Frontenac said. "We tussle for the advantage. Duschenau hopes to undermine me, finally to oust me. He may do it! I have kept you from the merchants' clutches, Robert; I have evaded the Jesuits, and I'll finance you in this emergency. But Duschenau is a riddle to which I have no answer. He may defeat us both!"

In August, as La Salle arranged his affairs, a vagrant *coureur de bois* brought him a letter from Tonty.

There had been many more desertions at Crêvecœur, Tonty wrote. The malcontents had organized as raiders; they had destroyed the fort and vowed to murder La Salle and all who supported him. When Tonty had defied them, they had started for Fort Miami on the St. Joseph, meaning to destroy that too. And the Indians were on the rampage, assaulting, torturing, killing in a

mad frenzy which might presage some vast general warfare such as Monso had prophesied.

La Salle turned back toward Crêvecœur, hastening,
his anxiety greater with each mile. Reaching Lake Peoria, he knew that his direst forebodings were justified.
The fort, the palisade, the blockhouses had been burned
to the ground.

Transfixed, he stared, trying to realize the extent of
this calamity—and Saget jogged his arm.

"Tonty's not here. He's dead." Saget was weeping.
"The Recollets, all dead."

"No, Peter," La Salle said. "Dry your tears. They're
alive, somewhere. We must rescue them!"

THE SEARCH

IX

La Salle soon saw that the ruin of Fort Crêvecœur had been but one part of a larger devastation. The country all around bore scars of recent battles. Remembering Tonty's letter, he could guess at what must have happened here:

The Iroquois had invaded from the north; the Kaskaskias, Miamis, and other minor western tribes had resisted—the inmates of Fort Crêvecœur had been caught between the two forces.

But had Tonty and the priests escaped?

"Yes," La Salle asserted, clinging to this conviction.

Down the Illinois River for weeks went his little rescue party, peering, searching, through a ravaged land where woods had been burned over, prairies trampled, Indian camps demolished. Quiet prevailed now; autumn sunshine gilded the days, and at night a comet streaked the sky with a tail of glowing radiance.

The comet? Saget eyed it superstitiously. An omen of more bad luck, Saget said.

La Salle reprimanded him curtly:

"The comet could as well be the omen of good luck, I shall believe it is!"

Their canoe moved steadily to the juncture of the Illinois with the Mississippi; and La Salle gazed in awe at that great, eddying current, yellow and turbulent, rolling, rolling southward.

The Father of Waters!

How often, how wishfully, he had dreamed of beholding it, of following it to its utmost end—and now there was no time for following, no time even for dreaming.

But Tonty, he felt, would not have passed on beyond this turning point.

"Tonty must have fled north from Crêvecœur," La Salle said. "We'll reverse our course and leave some mark for Tonty, on the off-chance that he may see it later."

On a wide strip of bark he drew the crude likeness of himself and his men, seated in a canoe, carrying a calumet. He nailed the signboard to a tall sycamore; and below the board he tied a penciled notice that he was heading up the Illinois again, toward the St. Joseph portage.

It was winter when the canoe nosed into the Kankakee marshes. The snow fell and drifted deeply; the wind howled stridently. On clear nights the comet shed its eerie light—and once it illumined a small, untenanted hut on the river bank.

Early next morning La Salle was inside the hut, stooping to pick up something from the clay floor.

A bit of pine planking—and cut with a saw!

"White men built this hut! The Indians have no tools, no saws!"

"Tonty?" Saget said.

"Perhaps," La Salle answered. "Let's pray it was Tonty and the priests."

In freezing weather they threaded the source streams of the Kankakee. Through the portage they were guided by the crosses which La Salle long ago had carved on tree trunks. Ice floes in the St. Joseph gashed the canoe; it could not be mended, and they had to go on afoot. After a month they neared Fort Miami; a week more, and they scaled the bluff and tottered, numb with cold, to the fort door.

La Forest was there—La Forest and his several men, who had been posted to await the *Griffin!*

La Salle greeted La Forest incredulously: "I had no hope of seeing you! I thought the fort had been destroyed."

"Raiders came from Crêvecœur," La Forest said, "and then the Indians. We hid from them. We have repaired the damage they did; we've hoarded some corn and guns; we've got timber for your boat."

"My boat?"

"A new boat, a substitute for the *Griffin.* You're

going down the Mississippi to the Gulf of Mexico, aren't you?"

"Yes," La Salle said. "Tonty and I, all of us."

"Where is Tonty?"

"Missing—but I'll find him."

The interior of the repaired fort was warm and bright with firelight. Too spent to talk, the wayfarers threw themselves down before the hearth and listened to La Forest as he told of the war which had raged like a scourge in this region. It was a riotous, relentless campaign begun by the Iroquois, aimed at exterminating the tribes of the Illinois. Skirmishes without number had been fought; and though the Five Nations had not quite rooted out their adversaries, they had spread much havoc.

Now the fighting had ceased.

"But it will never be entirely over," La Forest said. "This uncivilized land will never know peace."

La Salle sat, brooding and melancholy. If there was never to be peace, his vision of a glorious new France in America seemed doomed. Surely, though, the condition could be remedied, such disasters as the Indians' wars averted! He recalled what Governor Frontenac had done on Lake Ontario; how he had assembled the northern tribes, uniting them and, for an appreciable period, obtaining a truce.

Why couldn't that method be used again?

"It can," he thought. "Yes, the Indians can be taught the virtue of peace. Gradually, patiently, they can be made to see the folly of war. I'll have a council here in the west."

That night, many nights, he mused, planning his council. There were other things he would rather have planned—Tonty's rescue, the continuation, with Tonty, of his grand enterprise. But this, he felt, should be considered first. Of what benefit to the world was any exploration, even the most marvelous, if human beings busied themselves only with hatred and violence?

Sometimes he would get up from his bunk to stand at the window and look out at the comet, reflecting that the heavenly phenomenon was visible to people everywhere: to his mother in Rouen; to King Louis in the exquisite palace of Versailles, Frontenac in Quebec, the Abbé Jean Cavelier in Montreal—and to Tonty.

"For Tonty is not dead," he thought. "Splendid Tonty of the Iron Hand, I'll find him!"

Sometimes Saget stood at the window, too; and they spoke of the comet.

"At the Jesuit school I attended, we studied astronomy, Peter."

"Ah? I suppose you learned a good deal?"

"Very little. I should have studied harder."

"This comet, sir? It won't always hang there in the sky?"

"No, only briefly. A transitory span, Peter, like human existence, flashing from one void of darkness into the void again."

In March he set out from Fort Miami to tell the
Indians of his council. Around Lake Michigan, down
both banks of the St. Joseph, he trudged in sleet and
snow. The tribes were scattered; they had not recovered from the stunning blows of the Iroquois; driven
from their homes, the torn remnants wandered for-
lornly. La Salle had to track them to their straggling
camps and win their confidence with sacks of tobacco
and corn from the stock La Forest had prudently
hoarded. He asked them to confer with him in May at
a certain giant oak tree on the St. Joseph portage, near
the principal town of the Miamis. Because he was La
Salle, the white man who behaved like an Indian, they
heeded him.

Then, marooned in the marshes by a snowstorm, he
encountered a band of Fox Indians from Green Bay.
The Foxes had news of Tonty.

Tonty, they said, was at Michilimackinac!

Rejoicing, La Salle asked whether the Recollet friars
were with Tonty; but as to that, the Foxes could not
say. They had seen several priests at Green Bay—one
named Hennepin.

"Hennepin!" La Salle exclaimed.

"He has been among the Sioux on the Wisconsin
River. He is famous as a missionary. Hennepin preached
at Green Bay, on his way to Quebec."

"Go to Michilimackinac," La Salle bade the Foxes.
"Here is my gun, my knife—everything I have! But

hurry! Say to Tonty that in the summer, when I've held my council, I will meet him there."

The council convened in May, under the great oak. All the Illinois tribes were represented. La Salle came, wearing his red velvet cloak and a magnificent headdress of white plumes. His manner was calm and courtly, and he had brought the chiefs and sachems a gift of weapons —though these, he said, were for hunting, not for war.

He gathered the Indians about him and offered them the calumet. As they smoked he made a speech, praising the King of France and the *Onontio* Frontenac and outlining his idea of a confederation of the western and eastern tribes, similar to that of the Iroquois, strong enough to enable them to live in harmony with each other and without dread of attack from other quarters.

"I know this idea is novel to you," he said. "You must not adopt it at once. You must not reply without deep thought. Talk of it among yourselves; sleep on it. We will speak more tomorrow."

Next day they convened again, and the chiefs were ready with their reply. They had been impressed, they said, with the wisdom of La Salle; they were willing to accept the master of La Salle as the master of their people, willing to accept all the children of King Louis as their brothers. The Miamis, the Kaskaskias, the Kickapoos, all the tribes who had suffered so grievously, were weary of war; they would forge a bond of brotherhood for peace. They were shattered now, and feeble; but in unity they would wax strong. The Iroquois would fear to strike at them; no foe would assail them—thus, peace would reign in the land.

Like brothers the chiefs shook hands, and shook La Salle's hand. The calumet was refilled and lighted; treaty terms were discussed; the confederacy was consummated.

La Salle was jubilant. Perhaps this era of tolerance and sanity would not endure forever, but it was a step in the right direction; it might have lasting consequences.

"Finally," he thought, "with God's help, white men and red will be shown the way to permanent peace." . . .

And now he was free to go to Tonty at Michilimackinac!

It was a happy meeting. La Salle saw that Tonty looked thin and rather pale, but that his smile was undimmed.

"You are in good health, Tonty?"

"Never better, sir. Father Membré is here with me."

"And Father Ribourde?"

"No. I wish I could spare you this," Tonty said. "Father Ribourde was tomahawked, and his scalp flaunted as a trophy of war."

"Tomahawked? That holy old man!"

"When the Iroquois closed in, the Indians around our

fort turned on us, sir. With the pretext that we were allies of the Five Nations, they seized our gear and stores and dumped everything into the river. Most of our men had taken to their heels."

"Yes, I know," La Salle said. "Your letter was delivered to me. They were rogues, Tonty—rogues, just as you had called them."

"Savages is what they called themselves," Tonty said. " '*Nous sommes tous sauvages*' was their adieu to me, scrawled in blood on the blockhouse wall."

" '*We are all savages*'?"

"I wasn't sorry to lose them, sir. But afterward the priests and I, and the few faithful ones were in desperate plight. I went to the Illinois tribes and said I would fight on their side, for they had once been our friends. Well, I did fight—until I got an Iroquois dagger in my ribs, and was yanked by the hair before the enemy war lords. They voted on what to do with me—ought I be scalped or burned at the stake? While they were making up their minds, I slipped out of the net."

Then Tonty told how he had wanted to put a stop to the terrible, futile conflict; how he had shuttled back and forth between the two armies, trying to act as arbitrator. But by that time there was no hope of any understanding; he had seen that his prime duty was to save his little company before it was too late.

"We started up the river in a leaky canoe, and soon had to halt to plug the holes in our poor boat. As Father Ribourde paced the shore, saying his prayers, he was ambushed, pounced upon, killed. He died a martyr's death, with God's word on his lips."

Tonty paused. "A thing I can't forget is that the murderers were Indians to whom he had been kind—tribesmen of the Illinois, not of the Iroquois. Crazed with excitement, they didn't even recognize Father Ribourde, but dashed off, shouting that they had killed one more Iroquois."

From there Tonty's men had gone north to the Kankakee, where they built a hut.

"I was in that hut!" La Salle said. "I picked up a bit of pine from the floor."

Tonty smiled sadly. "It was the month of our greatest destitution. We were cold, hungry. We cut Father Ribourde's robe into squares and made shoes of it. We melted our one tin cup and molded bullets. Then, somehow, a Pottawattami Indian came along and discovered us and took us to a mission house of the Jesuits on the Kankakee. The Jesuits were generous and merciful— and I must say, sir, that the order has many good men in it."

"Yes, Tonty. Oh, yes!"

"They gave us food, medicine, a canoe. In the spring, when my wound had healed and the weather moderated, we paddled to Green Bay and on, to Michilimackinac."

"Tonty," La Salle said, out of a moment's silence, "searching for you, I saw the Mississippi—only a glimpse, but enough to confirm my determination to see it all.

But you have been through this ordeal; you may not want to see it with me. If so, I gladly release you from your bargain."

"No," Tonty said. "I'm the same fellow you hired as your lieutenant, in Paris."

"Are you?" La Salle smiled. "Then we'll go to the Gulf of Mexico together."

"IN THE KING'S NAME!"

X

From Fort Miami La Salle started again toward his long-sought goal.

The date was December 21, 1681. More than three years had elapsed since he had made his pact with the King; he had less than two years in which to redeem it. This time he would not break the journey to build either forts or boats, but would rely only on canoes for transportation, and travel fast.

With him now went Tonty, Father Membré, Saget, Nika, La Forest; eighteen Frenchmen, hand-picked by Tonty from among the survivors at Miami and Crêvecœur; eighteen Indian braves and ten squaws, three of whom had papooses strapped to their shoulders.

Tonty had been none too pleased about the women and children, but La Salle had spoken for them. The braves, he said, would not go without their wives; the three babies could not be separated from their mothers—

"And the squaws can cook for the party."

Tonty, who did not like to cook, had then withdrawn his objection.

Well-armed, the explorers went from the St. Joseph into Lake Michigan and down the Chicago River to a portage which led them to a northern branch of the Illinois. The weather was intensely cold. Where streams were frozen solidly over, the canoes were hoisted on wooden runners and served as sleds. In this way La Salle came to the town of La Vantum, once more encased in its cocoon of winter solitude, and to Lake Peoria. There the winds changed and were warmer, the ice thawed. Swiftly, through clearing currents, the canoes slid to the confluence of the Illinois with the Mississippi.

The Father of Waters! His excitement undimmed, La Salle saw it again, and identified for Tonty the sycamore on which he had nailed his signboard, before turning back on an errand of rescue.

Now, though, he could go forward with Tonty to the Gulf. The thought sobered him.

Down the Mississippi to the Missouri's mouth the canoes went, then to the inlet of the Ohio. The meat supply was dwindling. Below the Ohio the party landed to hunt. After that, landings were not uncommon; the prodigality of game was a constant temptation; over evening campfires the squaws cooked quantities of fowl and fish.

Each day the weather mellowed, the wind softened. The sun shone; trees had the tender green freshness of spring. With a feeling of affection, as if it were his own, La Salle looked at the country around him; in imagination he peopled the fertile plains, the noble forests with emigrants, farmers and artisans from old France who would settle happily in this new environment.

Perhaps his parleying with the western Indians would contribute to the comfort and security of these settlers.

"I hope so," he thought fervently.

The canoes approached the muddy mouth of the Arkansas River. A beating of drums sounded from the bank; a shower of arrows arched up from the rushes; and La Salle remembered that here Marquette and Joliet had met Indians more ferocious than any seen before. He remembered having said to Frontenac that Marquette should have tamed them—and he decided to go ashore.

"Give me the calumet, Tonty," he said. "Keep behind me, but out of sight."

Carrying the calumet, he walked quietly through the trees, aware that he was being watched by savages hidden in the underbrush. A circular open space in the forest was lined with small clay-daubed houses; in the circle squatted fifty Indians, very silent, waiting, as he came steadily, deliberately toward them.

At the rim of the circle he stopped and extended the calumet. The Indians did not stir, but scrutinized him with blank, unwavering eyes. He stuffed the bowl of the calumet with tobacco and, with the flint from his jacket pocket, lighted the tobacco, then put the stem of the pipe into his mouth and puffed a cloud of smoke. The Indians watched, motionless as statues, but there was a quiver of movement somewhere; and, looking back, he saw that many more slim brown men had slipped from among the trees; they were on all sides of him.

He puffed at the pipe, blew the smoke in rings from his mouth. Then, smiling, he extended the pipe at arm's length again.

A man got slowly up from the group of squatters. He was elderly, wrinkled, naked to the waist; in his braided black hair were three crow's feathers; he wore a short skirt of feathers, silver bracelets on his wrists and ankles, doeskin moccasins adorned with silver disks. Step by slow step he came toward the white intruder.

La Salle bowed and, in doing so, glimpsed a brightly polished, razor-sharp knife in the old Indian's hand.

La Salle straightened, stood smiling and calm, still offering the calumet.

After a moment the Indian, with a dramatic gesture, tossed down the knife and accepted the pipe of peace.

These natives of the Arkansas were Natchez; the old one was their chief. La Salle and his party spent three days in their village and were feasted and entertained. Father Membré erected a cross in front of the chief's house. The Indians watched with great interest, and nodded as the priest told them that the cross was Christianity's emblem, that henceforth they were to be subjects of the Christian King of France. They listened to Father Membré's preaching, knelt as he prayed; and, as a token of reverence, fenced off the cross with mats of reeds woven by their women.

"They are good people," said Father Membré, much gratified.

Farther south were the Taensas, another tribe of the Arkansas. Encouraged by his reception in the Natchez village, La Salle halted to visit with the Taensas, who also welcomed him and allowed a cross to be raised among them.

The Taensas were sun worshipers, living in dome-roofed houses, dressing picturesquely in white robes, fond of dancing and singing to tunes played on their simple musical instruments. Their chief was rich in jewels and ornaments, and in parting he gave La Salle a fine pearl necklace from his treasure closet—

"But I doubt that the Taensas were converted by my sermons," Father Membré said. "They are too gay and pleasure-loving."

La Salle remarked that Father Marquette shouldn't have been swerved from his course by the Arkansas Indians. "They would never have molested him."

"Can we be certain of that? No," Father Membré said. "You are unique in such matters, La Salle. You have a genius for conciliating men of an alien race. And what infinite afflictions, both physical and moral, might be avoided, if only more men of our own race were blessed with it!"

March 29 was Easter Sunday, piously observed with religious rites. La Salle himself had seldom felt more devout, more conscious of God's mercy and protection. All his adversities seemed to have dissolved, evaporating like the snows of winter—and the Taensas had told him that ten days of sailing would bring him to the sea.

Ten days? Why, they were nothing, compared to the harrowing hundreds of days he had toiled so tediously, compared to a lifetime!

Now the canoes were in southern waters; vines flowered on the river banks and carpeted the forest where fruit and nut trees blossomed, and pine trees swayed with skeins of gray-green moss. Now gulls flew screaming overhead, and beneath the water's surface exotic fish could be seen, turtles of monstrous size—and crocodiles!

Unbelieving, the travelers gaped at the crocodiles, their toothy jaws, their tough, leathery bodies and lashing tails. Could these animals be real?

"Oh, they're real enough," said Saget importantly. "Yes, I have read about crocodiles in books."

April 6 was a never-to-be-forgotten day, for then the travelers saw the broad channel of the Mississippi dividing abruptly into three smaller channels, like a ribbon fraying at its end. La Salle knew that the coast must be near by; he divided the party into three contingents, with Tonty directed to follow one channel, Nika another, himself the third.

An hour later Father Membré, in La Salle's contingent, leaned from the canoe, cupped water in his hand and tasted it.

"Salt!" he cried. "Salt!"

La Salle's heart leaped. Breathing deeply, he caught the unmistakable salt smell of the sea breeze.

"Men, we have come to the Gulf of Mexico! Paddle —faster!"

The paddles dipped, lifted, dipped again in a burst of furious energy—and there it was, at last, the immense, spreading, bright blue Gulf!

Father Membré shouted; the men shouted.

But La Salle was mute, too shaken by emotion to utter a word.

On April 9 all the party gathered at a spot on the Gulf's sandy border, where a thick-trunked tree had been topped and trimmed to make a tall column. Into the column an inscription had been carved: the arms of France, and the imposing legend:

LOUIS LE GRAND

ROI DE FRANCE ET DE NAVARRE, RÈGNE

LE NEUVIÈME AVRIL, 1682

As the Indian braves, the squaws and papooses gazed wide-eyed and wondering, a wooden cross was set in place beside the column, the Frenchmen drew up in soldierly ranks to chant a rousing *Te Deum* and fire their muskets, volley on volley, into the air.

La Salle stood before the column, in his left hand a parchment scroll; in his right, his unsheathed sword. He silenced the exuberant din of voices and guns, pointed his sword toward the cloudless springtime sky, and in solemn tones made his declaration:

"In the name of the most high, mighty, invincible and victorious Prince, Louis the Great, by the grace of God King of France and Navarre, I do now take possession of this country of Louisiana, the seas, harbors, ports, bays, towns, villages, mines, minerals, fisheries, streams and rivers, from the mouth of the Ohio, along the Mississippi, and the rivers which discharge themselves thereinto, from its source, to its mouth at the sea, or the Gulf of Mexico. . . . Of which, and of all else that is needful, I hereby take to witness those who hear me, and demand an act of the notary here present."

He paused, and gave the parchment scroll to Tonty for the affixing of the notary's seal.

"Saget," La Salle said, "the plate."

"Yes, sir." From under his coat Saget produced the metal box he had guarded for many months, through many vicissitudes.

La Salle opened the box; tilted it so that everyone might view its contents, a leaden plate engraved with the imperial insignia and the Latin phrase *Ludovicus Magnus Regnat.*

Then, kneeling, he buried the plate in earth at the foot of the cross.

XI

As HE turned from the column and the cross to reascend the Mississippi, La Salle felt that his work was but half done. This empire he had claimed for his King measured tens of thousands of square miles, an area more vast than the American possessions of all other European monarchs combined. But to be truly an asset to France, it must be colonized. Therefore, King Louis must plant colonies—and before the other monarchs could challenge his ownership.

It was La Salle's idea that, for a few years at least, the entire sweep of Louisiana might be watched over and controlled rather economically:

"I shall build and fortify a town at the Mississippi's mouth," he thought. "Tonty will build a town far north, on the Illinois. From these two well-placed bases, civilization can filter out until the country is dotted with French, Christian communities."

The base on the Gulf coast would be the more essen-
tial—and probably the more difficult to establish. But
Tonty's town was of first consideration.

"You must build a fort on Starved Rock, that great
impregnable cliff above the Illinois River," La Salle said
to Tonty. "As for the town, you already have the nu-
cleus for it in La Vantum, the Kaskaskias' big settlement. Make friends with the Indians, bind them to you
with kindness—and there is the beginning of your colony! This party of ours will soon disperse; the men will
be free to go their ways. La Forest and Father Membré
are going to Catarqui as managers of my scigniory. You
and I, with Saget and Nika, can concentrate on the task
at Starved Rock."

Tonty nodded. "Whatever you say. But I thought
you were off to Paris with your report to the
King."

"Later," La Salle replied. "Then I'll be able to tell the
King about our first colony—Fort St. Louis on the
Illinois."

The party dispersed at Michilimackinac; in December, La Salle and Tonty were at Starved Rock. All winter they labored, clearing timber from the summit of the
cliff; constructing a fort, storehouses, log cottages. By
spring Fort St. Louis was a reality, solid and stout,
perched like an eagle's nest above the river valley. In
April, looking down from the ramparts, La Salle could
see scores of Indians camping in the meadows and, at a
little distance, the streets of La Vantum, humming with

life and motion, as the natives flocked in from their winter hunting grounds.

"La Vantum is not a ghost town now," Tonty said. "Its population is perhaps twenty thousand. Because of you, the Indians are here; they think of you as their champion."

"I'll give them parcels of the land," La Salle said. "Yes, and all the men, red and white, who went with us to the Gulf shall have land to cultivate and farm. There is plenty of acreage for everyone."

Then a message came from Quebec to mar his pleasure in the new fort and colony:

Frontenac had been recalled from his office. Febvre de La Barre was Governor of Canada.

La Salle was dismayed—not so much for Frontenac as for himself. Frontenac, he knew, was a strong man, not easily foiled, with many supporters close to the throne.

"In a little time he may be reinstated," La Salle said to Tonty. "Frontenac tumbles only to light on his feet! But what will this mean to me and my enterprise?"

"Write to La Barre," Tonty suggested. "Sound him out."

"Yes, I will."

He wrote immediately to Governor La Barre, telling him of his plans, asking for some word of endorsement; when none arrived, he wrote again. Not long afterward he heard from Father Membré in Catarqui that La Barre would probably never deign to answer his letters; that La Barre had publicly spoken of the Sieur de La Salle as an imbecile dreamer, squandering money in the most fantastic of exploits.

Indignantly La Salle declared that he would go to Quebec and demand apologies. Insults to his intelligence he might have ignored—

"But when La Barre says that my discoveries amount to nothing, that, Tonty, I must throw in his teeth!"

"Yes, make him eat it!" said Tonty.

In the early autumn, with Saget and Nika, La Salle started for Quebec, and at the portage met the Chevalier de Baugis, a captain of dragoons, whom Governor La Barre had sent to seize Fort St. Louis. Smothering his wrath, La Salle penciled a note to Tonty: "Receive the Chevalier with all politeness." Going on to Catarqui, he found La Forest and Father Membré distraught by a rumor that the seigniory also was scheduled to fall into La Barre's clutches.

"This man is old and greedy, sir," La Forest said. "A bad choice for the post Frontenac held so efficiently."

"Why was Frontenac recalled?"

"He wrangled with Duschenau, the Intendant. It seems that governors must always dislike their subordinates. Courcelle did, you know."

"Yes," La Salle said, "and it wouldn't have been in Frontenac's character to compromise with Duschenau, or with anybody."

"So Duschenau complained to the King," La Forest said, "and the King booted them both out. They sailed for France a month ago."

"I'm sorry not to see Frontenac in Quebec; I had expected to."

"La Salle," Father Membré said, "my advice is that you hasten on to Paris without arguing the merits of La Barre's case against you. La Barre has a guilty conscience; probably he would not even face you. A ship is in the harbor now. Take it! You have friends in Paris. Your brother is there."

"Jean?"

"Yes, and Hennepin."

"Father Hennepin is writing a book about his American explorations," said La Forest.

Father Membré smiled. "Though the most of Hennepin's book may be devoted to boasting of his great attainments, he will certainly speak well of you, and of Frontenac too. What would you think of my going abroad with you? Perhaps I could be of help."

La Salle assented. "I'm sure you could. You, Saget, Nika, and I? I'll engage passage for the four of us."

In Paris he rented cheap lodgings in an obscure neighborhood and began to compose his report to the King.

It was an odd household. While La Salle worked at his papers, Saget cooked and cleaned; and Father Membré fared forth with Nika to the markets—the priest in his sandals and cowled gown, the Indian in rude gar-

ments of deerhide, causing much comment among pass-
ers-by in the city streets.

La Salle wrote rapidly, for he knew just what he
wanted to say. Having described his acquisition of Louisiana, he stressed the advantage of establishing a French
colony at the mouth of the Mississippi. He emphasized
that this was an auspicious moment: for several years
France and Spain had been on the verge of war; now, in
1684, the two nations were actually fighting. A port, a
substantial fortification on the Gulf would serve not
only as a stronghold for defense but also as a point from
which a French army could attack the Spaniards in
Mexico.

The report was hopeful in tone; he felt hopeful of the
King's response. Colbert, who on the previous occasion
had been cordial, was no longer minister of finance; but
Colbert's son, Seignelay, now had that high office. La
Salle made it quite plain that he himself would pay most
of the expenses involved in his scheme of colonization;
from the King he asked nothing more than one good
ship, a few cannon, and the authority to raise in France
a force of two hundred men. Surely, he thought, Seignelay would be like his father, wise and reasonable, looking favorably upon the Sieur de La Salle!

In fact, he was less worried about Seignelay's attitude
toward his carefully penned statements than about his
own attitude when he must appear in court and present
them. In the wilderness he had quite lost touch with the
elaborate niceties practiced in palaces and throne rooms.

For years his companions had all been rugged woodsmen or redskinned savages. How awkward and boorish
he would be in the royal chambers—a man who behaved
like an Indian rubbing elbows with a host of elegantly
clad, powdered and bewigged dandies!

Saget said he must get some new clothes.

"A velvet cloak or two," Saget said, "satin breeches,
buckled shoes. You're not so poor but that you can dress
up a bit! I'll snip your beard into a stylish shape; I'll cut
your hair and tie it behind, in the fashion. Between us
we can make you look very decent. Here, sir, sit in this
chair; I'll whet the scissors."

"Peter, you're priceless," La Salle said, sitting in the
chair. "You're always busy."

"Ha!" Saget tested the scissors blade with his finger.
"You used to say I was a lazy lout."

"Did I? Well, I was young then—as I am not now."

"No, sir. Forty, aren't you? And grizzled on head and
chin."

"All the years and miles you've followed me, Peter!
What a shame!"

"Why?" Saget said. "Why is it a shame?"

"Because in doing so you've missed the normal joys of
life, a home, a wife and children."

"But you've missed them, too, sir."

"With me it has been different. I've had this engross-
ing wish, this obsession." La Salle smiled. "Long ago at
La Chine I was in love with a girl, or thought I was. She
was pretty; I might have married her. But then I talked

with my brother. Jean said I could scarcely have both a wife and a career. What woman, he asked, would wish to marry a footloose wanderer like me? No, I must decide which I wanted most, the pretty girl or my liberty. So I put the pretty girl out of my mind forever."

Saget poised the scissors. "And you have not regretted it?"

"Not once. Jean was right. But you, Peter, might still marry. You could stay in France—"

"Neglecting my duty? Sir, you offend me! Sit straighter, please, and don't gossip so much. I should hate," said Saget, "to lop off a piece of your ear."

When La Salle went to see Seignelay, he learned that La Barre's treatment of him was known at court.

"The Canadian Governor has written most uncharitably about you," Seignelay said.

"Do you believe the Governor?"

"No," Seignelay said. "His charges are obviously exaggerated. Besides, I have heard from other persons of your trip down the Mississippi."

La Salle tapped the document he carried. "I've told all that in here."

"The Count de Frontenac is in Paris; he praises you."

"I have not yet seen Frontenac."

"You may not; he is in seclusion. But only temporarily," Seignelay said. "A remarkable man, the Count; he will rise from this eclipse. He may even be reappointed at Quebec—who knows? At any rate, Frontenac, in seclusion, is doing his best for you. I can promise that the King will attentively read your statement."

La Salle asked whether he might have an audience with the King.

"If it can be arranged," Seignelay said, "I will notify you."

While La Salle waited and hoped for the audience, La Forest came to Paris. La Forest had been ejected from Catarqui, which the Governor's troops had seized and occupied.

"It was the same with Tonty," La Forest said. "Tonty got your message; he was polite to the Chevalier Baugis. But Baugis wasn't so sweet-mannered; Baugis chased him out."

"Where is Tonty?"

"On the Illinois, with the Indians. Baugis is no hand with the tribes, sir. He detests them, and they detest him."

"I shall request the King, through his minister, to right these wrongs, La Forest," La Salle said. "You remain here until I know what can be done."

A week later he had his audience with Louis XIV.

Escorted by Seignelay into the King's presence, he bowed before that august, majestic figure seated in splendor on the golden dais. Louis the Magnificent, the Sun! Would he be generous now to one who had served him so unstintingly?

The King was generous.

He had read the statements of the Sieur de La Salle; he was convinced of their truth, delighted that his American dominions had been so enormously expanded. He grieved that his Governor of Canada should have unlawfully taken over the forts Frontenac and St. Louis; he would instantly dispatch La Forest to Quebec to recover the properties in La Salle's name.

Indeed, all that La Salle requested of him was granted —and more. The colony at the terminus of the Mississippi would be planted. La Salle would be given, not one ship, but four good vessels, the company of soldiers, also mechanics and carpenters, and sufficient provisions. It was the royal wish that six clergymen, Recollets and Sulpicians, have the spiritual guidance of the colony, these six to include the friars Zenobe Membré and Anastase Douay, and the Abbé Jean Cavelier. . . .

With signed and sealed commissions the grant would be formally issued. . . .

"I could not adequately thank the King," said La Salle to Seignelay, in an anteroom of the palace. "I was dumb with happiness. You interceded for me. How can I show my gratitude to you?"

"Well, there is one small matter—"

"Yes? What is it?"

"I should like Captain Beaujeu to be in command of the ships from La Rochelle to the Gulf."

"Captain Beaujeu?"

"A veteran of the royal navy, an expert navigator. You may set the route; Beaujeu will command the crews.

After the ships reach America, you will have sole authority in everything."

La Salle hesitated only a moment. "It shall be as you
say, sir."

At his modest lodgings he roused Saget.

"We're going to Rouen, Peter, to visit my mother. I
have a pearl necklace for her."

"The necklace of the Taensas' chief? Ah, that will
just suit Madame Cavelier." Saget's black eyes sparkled.
"You'll visit your brother Paul too? Your sister Marie
and her good husband? Your nephews?"

"Colin and Crevel. They must be big boys now. Yes,"
La Salle said. "Colin is almost fifteen. And Crevel?—
why, he's twenty-one! Not a boy at all. A man."

VOYAGE IN STRANGE WATERS

XII

La Salle sat at a desk in the window of the water-front inn. The morning was brilliant with sunlight, shimmering with heat. Glancing up from pen and ink pot, he could see the La Rochelle harbor and four docked vessels—

His vessels! Proudly he named them over: the *Joly*, man-of-war, forty guns; the *Belle*, frigate, six guns; the *Amiable*, flyboat, laden with food, iron, building materials; the *Falcon*, ketch, carrying ammunition.

On the cobbled pavement of the wharf, men were loitering. *His* men, mechanics, laborers, soldiers. In all, the voyagers would be two hundred and eighty persons —more than he had reckoned on, for there had been numerous volunteers.

Henri Joutel was a volunteer, a young man of breeding and wealth from Rouen.

123

"I've heard about your colony," Joutel had said. "I'd like to join it."

La Salle had been pleased. "I wish you would! You're just the sort of colonist I'm looking for."

So a hammock for Joutel had been swung aboard the *Joly*, in the cabin with La Salle himself, Father Membré, Father Douay, and the Abbé Cavelier.

Now La Salle was writing a letter of farewell:

Rochelle, 18 July, 1684
Madame, My Most Honored Mother,
At last, after having waited a long time for a favorable wind, and having had a great many difficulties to overcome, we are setting sail. . . .

The door creaked on its hinge; La Salle laid down his pen.

"Peter?"

"Yes, sir." Saget stepped in and shut the door behind him. "Well, I did as you told me; I talked with Captain Beaujeu. He says the two boys can be berthed on the *Joly*."

"Good!"

Saget paused. "You still think they should go?"

"You mean that you think they shouldn't?"

"Maybe. I don't know." Saget scratched his head. "Our prospects do seem very bright, eh? But children on such a trip—"

La Salle was irritated. "My nephews are not children.

Crevel is older than you were when you first started for America; and Colin—"

"Oh, Colin will be all right, sir, young though he is. A mild, tractable lad, if ever I saw one, quite like his father, your brother Paul. It's Crevel I fret about, Crevel de Moranget. Tall, handsome; yes, but with his nose in the air. Your sister Marie has spoiled him."

"Nonsense!" Suddenly angry, La Salle thumped his fist on the desk. "I want no criticism from you of either my sister or her son."

As Saget was silent, La Salle closed his eyes and thought of Rouen, his mother's house, that recent scene at the dinner table, when Crevel had so relentlessly entreated him, and all the family had sided with the boy:

"You said I could go to America someday! You promised!"

Again and again Crevel had repeated it, with Marie, Paul, everybody chiming in:

"Yes, Robert, you did. You promised."

And he could not deny it, that was the worst of the thing. Years ago, always, La Salle had said that someday his nephew could share his adventures—La Salle and de Moranget! But each time, having said it, he had forgotten. How amazing that Crevel had never forgotten, that Crevel seemed to have lived only for the day!

"And Colin too! Colin—"

Startled, he had looked across the table at the slender, fair-haired Colin and realized abruptly that he scarcely knew him, that indeed he had little acquaintance with either of these relatives of his; except for occasional, brief glimpses, years apart, they were as strangers to him. Crevel and Colin, members of his party?

"I would be nervous, afraid—"

"Why?" they asked, in chorus, the nephews, Marie, Paul, everybody. "Of what? You don't doubt that you'll succeed in establishing your colony?"

"No, I will succeed."

"Well, then?"

Gazing at them all, their eager, smiling faces, he had seen how implicitly they trusted him—and how slightly they understood what the American wilderness was like, what he had done there and had yet to do. Of course, it could not have been otherwise; nothing in their own sphere could have trained them to understand a sphere so foreign. He had told them stories, and they had listened—but as if the stories were fiction, thrilling, exciting, and never without a happy ending.

"You said we could go, Colin and I."

"Yes, Robert."

Well, he could not refuse them—for when had they ever refused him anything? And he *would* succeed; he had no doubt of it! . . .

But, in the moment of relenting, he had been sorry for this added responsibility. . . .

He opened his eyes and glared at Saget. "No harm will come to my nephews."

"Better keep them from under Beaujeu's feet, then. Doesn't Beaujeu remind you of that old Father Dollier, the Sulpician?"

"No," La Salle said gruffly.

"He has a poor opinion of you, sir. Told the crew that you're a stupid Norman oaf, fit only to command Indians and schoolboy brats."

"Beaujeu's a Norman himself."

"He brags that he's seen the world."

"He hasn't seen the New World."

"No, but he says he'd wager that with his brains he could learn more about America in an hour than you've learned in eighteen years. And I just can't stomach this volunteer Duhaut," Saget continued morosely, "the one with the valet, L'Archevêque. Or Hiens, the German— he used to be a buccaneer. Or Liotot, the surgeon, muttering in corners with Teissier, the fishy fellow who's to pilot the frigate—"

"Stop!" La Salle's fist thumped, and the ink pot tottered. "Get out, you fool!"

"Why, I was merely—"

"You bawl like an orphaned calf! Take your doleful recital elsewhere!"

When Saget had tiptoed, crestfallen, from the room, La Salle sat frowning, thinking:

So Beaujeu had a poor opinon of him? Probably it was no poorer than his own opinion of Beaujeu. If Beaujeu resented having only one-half the command, La

Salle felt just as strongly in the matter. The situation was ticklish for both men, agreeable to neither.

"We'll be like acrobats balancing on a tightrope, Beaujeu and I," La Salle mused. "Well, I'll not shove Beaujeu off—but he must be as considerate of me!"

As for Duhaut, Hiens, Liotot, Teissier, he had the haunting memory of a frigid night at Crêvecœur, an explosion in the darkness and Tonty's voice chiding him with recklessness, lack of discrimination.

"Therefore, I've tried now to exercise shrewd judgment."

The time, though, had been limited. Unable to investigate the qualifications of all recruits, he had accepted some of them impulsively or on the recommendation of Seignelay in Paris. It was possible that among them might be a few incompetents, laggards, drones—

"But no rogues," he thought. "If Tonty were here, he would see they are not rogues!"

He stared out of the window at the harbor, the four fine ships, and his spirits lifted. Grasping the pen, he finished the letter:

. . . Be sure that you will always find me with a heart full of the feelings which are due to you, Madame, my Most Honored Mother, from your most humble and most obedient servant and son,

De La Salle.

Then at the bottom of the sheet, he wrote a post-script:

My brother, my nephews, and all the others greet you, and take their leave of you.

They sailed on July 24, and on August 20 Captain Beaujeu sighted the Island of Madeira.

"We'll anchor for fresh water and flour," he said.

La Salle dissented; it would be unwise to anchor. Spanish boats often made port on the island; the people there might tell the Spaniards about the Gulf-bound French vessels.

"The more secretly we move, the safer," La Salle said. "Besides, our supplies of all kinds are ample. Why, we're not a month out from La Rochelle!"

Beaujeu bowed to this decision—but sullenly. It was the first altercation between the two halves of the command, and La Salle had won it. The vessels sailed past Madeira; Beaujeu stood, immobile and uncommunicative, behind the helmsman; La Salle retreated into his cabin to brood over maps and charts.

On September 6 the *Joly*, leading the small fleet, crossed the Tropic of Cancer; and at midmorning Crevel de Moranget, disheveled, infuriated, rushed in upon his uncle.

The crew, Crevel said, had a great cask of sea water on deck; they were flinging the passengers into it, one by one—and under the captain's eyes, while Beaujeu watched indulgently! Joutel had been ducked, Colin was at this moment in the cask; Crevel, snatched at, had broken away:

"I'll not submit to it! They're coming to get *you*; the captain told them to!"

La Salle strode from the cabin.

Yes, there were the sailors, doubled over with mirth; the passengers, laughing rather less heartily, some of them wet from head to foot; and Captain Beaujeu looking on, casually smiling.

A sailor lunged toward La Salle, stretching a grimy, calloused paw. "Your turn, sir! Your turn!"

La Salle drew himself to full height. "Don't lay a finger on me! Stop this outrageous clowning, this horseplay!"

The sailor blinked. "Why, it's the custom, sir! A ship swings under the Tropic o' Cancer line—then it's a good ducking and a noggin o' rum all 'round, and an oath sworn that those in the cask will do the ducking next time—"

"I forbid it!"

"But the master's for it. The master said—"

"The master?"

"Captain Beaujeu."

"I am master here. Empty that cask."

The sailor looked astonished, and Captain Beaujeu's smile was sardonic.

"Monsieur La Salle, you flout a tradition of the sea.

It is but innocent sport, to spell the boredom of our voyage."

"I forbid it," La Salle repeated stonily.

"To do so is to commit an error—as any mariner would know. However you are not a mariner, eh?" Beaujeu shrugged. "Men, you have heard Monsieur La Salle. Empty the cask."

La Salle strode back into his cabin and slammed the door.

As his wrath subsided, he saw that he had indeed committed an error; that, by it, Beaujeu had scored. Innocent sport? . . . Once long ago, and also on shipboard, a little priest had cried out against music, dancing. In La Salle's ears rang the echo of a voice, his own, raised to reprimand the meddler. . . .

Why had he been so angry just now? Was it because of Crevel, embarrassment for Crevel, who had run, like a coward, a mollycoddle, from the cask? Colin had not protested, and had not been hurt. The ducking wouldn't have hurt Crevel, either—it might have been good for him! Crevel was always showing himself scornful of the crew, holding aloof—as Saget had said, "nose in the air."

"But that wasn't what angered me," La Salle thought. "It was Beaujeu, his wish to humiliate me. And he did humiliate me—though in a way he may not have anticipated."

The door opened on Joutel and the Abbé Cavelier.

"The sailors are grumbling," Jean said. "Grumbling about you to Beaujeu; he seems to enjoy it. You spoke indiscreetly, Robert. A little sea water is better than a lot of mutiny."

"Yes," La Salle said. "Yes, I am thinking of that."

THE WIDE BLUE GULF

XIII

ON SEPTEMBER 20 the *Joly* broke her voyage to land at Petit Goave on the Island of Santo Domingo.

La Salle was chagrined; he had designated the more accessible harbor at Port de Paix as the landing place. But he said nothing. Since the incident of the ducking, he had kept his balance on that tightrope between himself and Beaujeu.

The *Joly* anchored at noon, the *Amiable* and the *Belle* at twilight. The *Falcon* did not come; there was no word of her. Through the night La Salle waited and in the morning knew that the *Falcon* would never come.

The ketch had been set upon and captured by Spanish pirates.

This was inexcusable, and La Salle's temper slipped its leash. He raged at Beaujeu: "It is the result of your

133

insolent policy, your wish to demonstrate a superiority over me!"

Beaujeu arched his eyebrows. "Oh, no! These things happen—"

"Through negligence!"

Beaujeu murmured that Monsieur La Salle, who was not a mariner, seemed to bear the curse of violent passions and an unbridled tongue: "Let us reconcile ourselves. Petit Goave is a pleasant town for a little holiday."

But the pleasant town of Petit Goave was gripped now by a fever epidemic. Within the week Beaujeu, La Salle, and most of the party were stricken.

In a squalid native hut, nursed by Saget and Nika, La Salle plucked at his straw pallet, moaned, and asked about the men.

"Are they sick, Saget? Dying?"

"Yes, or drunk and deserting," Saget said. "The natives have rum to sell; our fellows are swilling it down by the pint, to stave off the fever. A cure worse than the disease, sir."

"We must get away," La Salle said. "We must get away—"

In late November, their ranks depleted, the voyagers sailed for the Isle of Pines, and from there to Cuba. The stormy season had begun; the three ships were battered by gales, sluiced by torrential rains. On December 13 they were in the Gulf of Mexico, and La Salle, still feeling the effects of fever, paced the *Joly's* deck and scanned the gray line of barely visible coast.

"Proceed cautiously, Captain Beaujeu. Beware of shoals."

His tone was courteous; he had studiously made it so, but Beaujeu turned on him:

"You have navigated a ship in the Gulf, sir?"

"No," La Salle said. "I have not."

"Ah? I shall proceed then as I think best."

Beaujeu told the helmsman to proceed westward. La Salle paced. The gray line of coast varied little, if at all; it was thin and indistinct, shrouded by fog and rain.

"And what exactly, Monsieur La Salle, is the longitude of this spot where you planted your cross, your column?"

La Salle sighed; the question was asked to annoy him. "I don't know the longitude."

"You don't know!"

"I have said so frankly from the start; said so to the King, to Seignelay, and to you. I know the latitude—"

"But you thought the longitude of no importance?"

"Certainly not! I tried to learn it. My instruments were imperfect."

"Oh, yes, your instruments!" Beaujeu's voice crackled with contempt. "I think it would be wise to head back to France, for we are sailing without a destination!"

"The mouth of the Mississippi is our destination. I will recognize it when I see it."

"But you do not see it now?"

"No," La Salle said. "No."

Sailing without a destination? . . . Day after day he strained his eyes, hating himself for his ineptitude, praying that by a miracle knowledge would be revealed to him. Sometimes Indians in canoes darted out from that gray shore, came within hailing distance.

"Where is the Mississippi?" Leaning over the rail, he queried them. "Where is the great river?"

The Indians never answered. The *Joly* plied on westward, with the frigate and the flyboat trailing in her wake.

He thought: "We may be going too far, going past it. I'm not sure. . . . But if we veered about and went east again—I would not be sure, either."

It was January, February, warm weather in this southern climate. He could not eat or sleep. Day and night he was at the rail, desperately trying to read the riddle of that monotonous gray-green coast.

At last he said: "Captain Beaujeu, we must have sailed beyond the river's mouth. We will have to land in the first available harbor."

"Yes," Beaujeu said imperturbably. "It would be as well to land."

The harbor they sighted was narrow, flanked by reefs; but Beaujeu brought the *Joly* nicely in. The frigate and the flyboat were standing off. Hastily disembarking, La Salle made soundings and arranged an aisle of upright stakes through which the smaller vessels

might be steered to shore. The frigate maneuvered her
way with skill, beaching beside the *Joly*. But the pilot
of the flyboat, as if perversely, swerved her a little from
the staked aisle—just enough to send the vessel afoul of
submerged rocks.

There was a sudden thud, then a rending noise,
screams.

The flyboat keeled over, sank slowly, as passengers
and crew leaped from her tilting deck and swam fran-
tically from the whirlpool which would have sucked
them under.

La Salle was aghast. The *Amiable* lost!—going down,
down, the waters closing above her. . . .

"The pilot did it!" Joutel exclaimed.

"Purposely!" said Jean Cavelier.

"It was flagrant defiance of your signals, La Salle,"
Father Membré said. "It could have been nothing else."

Even Beaujeu was appalled, shouting that the pilot
had transgressed every tradition, every rule of the sea
and his profession; the pilot was a dastard—Beaujeu
would have him clapped in irons for his crime.

Only La Salle was silent, watching the people from
the *Amiable* scramble ashore, shake themselves, col-
lapse, gasping, in the sand, and Saget moving among
them, counting to see that none was missing.

Presently Saget looked up. "All here, sir."

"Thank you, Peter," La Salle said. "Well, we must
have a fire to dry them by."

A fire was kindled, a rude camp pitched, a meal

cooked and eaten. Night was coming on. Behind this ragged strip of yellow-white beach, shadows mantled a black, moss-draped forest; overhead the sky was slate-colored, striped with the eerie, flapping flight of grotesque gray pelicans; in front lapped the long gray waves, littered with floating debris.

Darkness deepened; some of the party slept, hollowing out beds in the sand, burrowing under the sand, like prairie dogs, like chipmunks.

La Salle went to his cabin in the *Joly*, got out pen and paper, and sat at the table. He must write a report to Seignelay. The ship was quiet; he did not hear Captain Beaujeu until he was on the very threshold.

"Monsieur La Salle? I did not think to see you thus engaged."

"I am computing my losses, a list for Seignelay."

"They are quite formidable, your losses?"

"Yes. The ketch, the flyboat, and all their contents: cannon, grenades, muskets, ammunition, utensils, tools, a forge, a mill, two tons of iron and two of lead, sixty barrels of wine, most of the grain, blankets, clothing, boxes of medicine—"

Beaujeu nodded. "Probably you are dejected; you will give up this experiment."

"No," La Salle said. "No, I am not dejected."

"Monsieur La Salle, I will deliver your list to the minister of finance in Paris. I leave tomorrow—or as soon as possible."

"You leave!"

"On the *Joly*, with my crew. I contracted to bring your party to the Gulf coast and I have done that, eh? But I made no rash avowals to stay in the God-forsaken country."

"Captain Beaujeu, the *Joly* is my ship, by the King's grant."

"I think not, sir. It is the property of the royal navy, lent to you for a period now expiring. As an officer of the royal navy, I must restore the *Joly* to her rightful custodians."

La Salle got to his feet. "Captain Beaujeu, leave on the *Joly*, with your crew. Leave tomorrow, as soon as possible, whenever you like—and good riddance! Deliver my report to Seignelay. Tell him all that I have not done, my failures, blunders, and omissions. But tell him, too, that my colony at the mouth of the Mississippi, where I planted the cross, the column, the King's arms, will eventually be established."

THE DIFFICULT DAYS

XIV

IT WAS easier for La Salle to compute what remained to him than what he had lost. This list was much shorter: one ship, the *Belle*, carrying six cannon and several dozen barrels of supplies, and one hundred and eighty persons—most of whom Saget had described as "fit for nothing but eating."

"The month is March, 1685," La Salle thought, "and I am on terrain which seems totally unfamiliar."

Nevertheless, he would not admit, even to himself, any doubt of an ultimate success. He had miscalculated the position of the Mississippi; yes, that was true, and he still was confused as to whether he had come too far or not far enough. It was true that he could have made good use of the other three ships, their rigging and cargo, and that a majority of his people were inexperienced and badly frightened.

"But I have Saget, Nika, the friars Membré and

Douay, my brother Jean, my nephews, and Joutel," he thought. "And I have my commission from the King which, in honor, I must fulfill."

In sinking, the *Amiable* had burst her seams; now scraps of planking, broken masts and spars were washing ashore. La Salle salvaged all such lumber and had huts and canoes built with it. He noticed a small stream, not more than a creek, winding down to the Gulf through sand and sedge. Perhaps the rivulet was one of the Mississippi's thousand branches; and by exploring it, the great river could be located. As soon as the camp on the beach had been organized into some semblance of orderliness, he named Joutel to manage it; and with fifty men he went to survey the area.

He was absent a month—and he did not see the Mississippi; the small stream had no connection with the Father of Waters. But, returning, he told Joutel that he had discovered a much more sheltered spot for their temporary headquarters:

"A river lies to the east of us; I have called it *La Veche*, the Cow, because of the wild cattle roaming its banks. La Veche flows into Matagorda Bay, which has a clean, drained beach, ideal for the erecting of a fort."

Meanwhile Joutel had fared rather badly. He said he was sorry that Beaujeu hadn't taken with him on the *Joly* certain of his cronies:

"I don't like Duhaut, sir, or Hiens, the German. Especially, I am repelled by that strutting, blustering surgeon, Liotot."

And Indians lurked in the pine woods, Joutel said. At night the Indians had crept upon the camp and stolen guns and a barrel of grain. Poisonous snakes wriggled through the grass and weeds; many persons had been bitten by the reptiles; one case had been fatal.

"And ten men have disappeared, sir."

"Deserted?" La Salle asked.

"It may be. One day they were here; the next, gone. Singly or in pairs—as if the earth had opened and swallowed them. These disappearances have created an atmosphere of mystery and terror, which the priests are striving to assuage with prayers and sermons."

No time was wasted in moving the party to Matagorda Bay. The weather was sweltering; the sun merciless; the work so arduous that thirty of the strongest men were prostrated, dropping and dying in their tracks. But La Salle was sustained by what seemed a superhuman energy. He bore the brunt of the task, hewing trees; planing timbers; completing dwellings, storehouses, a fort; then digging gardens, which he sowed with corn and vegetables.

The safety of his people was always his primary concern—and he was disturbed that Indians should lurk also in the woods around Matagorda Bay. Often he must pause in the midst of his building and hurry in pursuit of savages who had let fly a peppering of arrows at the new fort. If overtaken, the Indians could be pacified; but La Salle was puzzled that the furtive sniping should not abate.

He talked of this with the Abbé Cavelier.

"The savages ought to know by now that I'm not an enemy, Jean. The word should have spread among them."

"Yes. Of course," Jean said, "most of our Frenchmen have never before seen an Indian—and some are inclined to harass them, as if it were a form of sport, like bear-baiting. Crevel does that."

"Crevel de Moranget?" La Salle was amazed. "I did not know it!"

"You can't know everything; you are too busy. Last week Crevel went out to shoot crocodiles. He saw a small band of Indians. They accosted him; he fired and wounded one of them."

"But the Indians must have fired?"

"Afterward. Crevel's was the first shot. Robert," Jean said, "there's no blinking the fact that our nephew is an arrogant, willful youth. You're fond of him—and I am fond of him; but he is unpopular with the men, and his frequent misdemeanors vex and worry me. Why did you bring him?"

"I had to," La Salle said. "I just had to."

"Well, we're saddled with him; we must make the best of it." Jean looked grave. "You're starting again to hunt for the cross and the column?"

"Yes, in the fall."

"I suggest you take Crevel with you—and Colin; both boys."

"I will," La Salle said. "And you also, Jean. I'm waiting only until the *Belle* has been sailed up into the bay and anchored. As long as we have the frigate, we're in no real danger; for we could always embark and ascend the Mississippi in her to Canada."

"When we have found the Mississippi? Or," Jean said, "We could sail for France?"

La Salle shook his head. "Beaten? Acknowledging defeat? Never! Nothing seems more unlikely."

On October 31, with Jean, the two boys, Saget, and thirty other companions, he left the fort in Joutel's hands and went on a second exploration of this southern wilderness. West, then south, then east, he plunged through the tropical forests, through rainstorms and hurricanes, fording innumerable small rivers, anxiously interrogating the Indians:

"Where is the *big* river? The Mississippi?"

They could not tell him.

He quizzed Saget and was irritated at his replies.

"You saw the place, Peter. Don't you remember it?—how the channel divided like the tines of a fork; how the land flattened out into swamps and bayous, and the wind smelled of salt, and there, suddenly, was the Gulf?"

Saget remembered vividly. "But we were seeing it all from above, sir, from the north. Now nothing looks the same."

"Peter, you numskull! You have the intellect of a gnat!"

"Yes, sir. I think Beaujeu may have set us down hundreds of miles west of our cross and column."

"Ridiculous, ridiculous!"

But he continued to thrust eastward, baffled at the strangeness about him, angry at himself for being so angry with Saget.

"I am the numskull, not Peter," he thought. "By my own inefficiency I've got us into this impasse. By my own effort and ingenuity, I must get us out."

In February they came to a river of such dimensions that he was briefly deluded. The Mississippi! He built a palm-thatched lodge on the bank, posted twenty of his men in the lodge and hurried with the rest to the river's mouth.

But this was not the Mississippi, nor even a tributary of it.

He retraced his steps to the lodge.

The men were gone. There was merely a pile of logs and brown fronds, curling in the sun.

On March 31, 1686, gaunt and tattered, he trudged into the fort on La Veche. With him were Jean, the nephews, Saget, ten of the men.

"Where are the others?" Joutel said.

"They're—somewhere. I'll find them when I go out again. And I will find the Mississippi."

The *Belle* was at the bottom of the Gulf of Mexico, a sodden wreck, an irreparable loss.

He could scarcely believe the pilot, Teissier, who confessed it. He had sent the frigate out of the bay, to

skirt the Gulf, thinking that from this angle the Mississippi's three channels might be glimpsed.

"Proceed cautiously," he had warned. "Beware of
shoals."

"Yes, sir." . . .

And here was Teissier, saying that the *Belle* had sunk.

"Your crew, Teissier?"

"All drowned."

"But you're alive."

"I swam. I'm a good swimmer."

"You're a good pilot when you're not drinking. You
had filched wine from Joutel's stores; you were drunk."

Teissier began to whimper, wiping his flushed face
on a ragged sleeve. "So you blame me for what I
couldn't prevent! You blame me for what's only one
more of your miserable errors! It's just as Beaujeu said,
as Liotot and Duhaut are saying—"

"Silence!"

"No craft could have stayed afloat in those devilish
waves, those slashing gales. I did my best—"

"Stop!" La Salle thundered. "Begone, you drunken
traitor!"

He sat thinking, wondering bleakly what could be
done. The months had exacted their toll of his people;
illness had ravaged them; they were undernourished,
lonely, discouraged. Without relief they would inevita-
bly languish and die.

But where could relief be obtained?

He thought, then, of Tonty.

"Tonty is in Illinois. I'll send him a letter, tell him to go to Canada and get the things we need— No! I myself will go to Tonty and bring him back with me!"

But to find Tonty in Illinois, the Mississippi must first be found. . . .

"Very well," La Salle thought. "The Mississippi. It cannot elude me this time!"

On April 22, after hearing mass and invoking divine guidance, he started with twenty men. He had little equipment: a few guns, a few pounds of powder, two axes, some beads and knives as gifts for the Indians. He traveled in a northeasterly direction, traveled for untold miles, in the torrid heat of summer, in country ever more perplexing and sinister. Two of the men succumbed to sunstroke; two died of snakebite; one was devoured by a crocodile—four disappeared.

In mid-October he led the remnants of the weary group to the fort on La Veche.

"Did you find the Mississippi?" Joutel asked.

"No," he said. "No, Joutel. But I will do so—next time."

XV

Autumn was beautiful that year and, somehow, his hopes were high. It seemed incredible that his previous searchings had been fruitless—

"Ah, but I was not properly prepared."

Observation, reflection, the study of his maps and charts had convinced him that Captain Beaujeu had, indeed, set him down several hundred miles wide of the goal—

"Well, it was my fault as much as Beaujeu's; perhaps more."

The Mississippi must be northeast of Matagorda Bay— it had to be; it could not be elsewhere.

Therefore, by bearing undeviatingly in that direction, ever northeast, he would reach the Mississippi, which was the route, the only one now, to the Illinois and Tonty, to help for his people—finally to success.

In the last weeks of October he prepared the fort so

that the inmates might be as snug as possible while they waited for the reinforcements which would come to them from Canada. He constructed a palisade between the fort and the forest. Game was plentiful and the garden patches had yielded a good harvest; he made sure that all this bounty of nature was preserved and stored for the winter months ahead.

Dealing with the Indians in the vicinity, he got from them the promise to maintain peace with his people, and an agreement to furnish him with five horses for his journey. In November he gathered up everybody's wearing apparel and had the old garments washed, re-tailored, and furbished, the guns polished, the sword blades honed.

Then it was the Christmas season, which he bade the priests to celebrate in the most solemn and devout manner; and during the holidays he held sessions of public prayers and spoke to the assemblage of his determination to protect all his followers, no matter what the cost to himself.

At length he was ready to choose his traveling companions.

As before, he would take his brother, his nephews, Saget, Nika, Father Douay. But this time Joutel must go:

"Father Membré, you will preside here."

"I will," said Father Membré.

"I have named seven; I want ten more."

He chose the ten—and Liotot, who was not among them, came to him in the evening, protesting.

It was odd, Liotot said, that he had been passed over. Yes, and Duhaut, De Marle. Were they not gentlemen of rank and prestige in France, better born probably than the Sieur de La Salle? And what of Teissier and the German Hiens? Why was it that, starting out, La Salle should wish an escort consisting of his relatives, his intimates, a red barbarian, a sniveling, shaved-pate Recollet friar?

But perhaps there was some secret in the wind? Perhaps an undivulged detail of Monsieur La Salle's elaborate arrangements was a way by which he and his escort could slip quietly to some wonderful refuge, abandoning the poor, patient people in the fort—

La Salle interrupted. "I have not abandoned you yet, have I? I have gone, and have returned."

"Perhaps the way was not then available. We do not know what you have done on these trips. We do not know but that you have a ship concealed somewhere." Liotot shrugged. "We know nothing except what you tell us. Our lot is to suffer in this hideous desolation."

"Suffer! Do you think, Liotot, that *I* have not suffered; have not been hungry and thirsty, tired and troubled? You talk of your desolation. Have you no thought of mine?"

"That, sir, is of your own making," Liotot said. "And ours is of your making, too. You have condemned us to this extremity. We put our lives in your hands and you have betrayed us. We fear you may betray us even further."

"I've never betrayed you, never will!"

"Then prove it by letting me select some of the personnel of your party. The Caveliers, Father Douay, Joutel, the Indian Nika, and that odious little Saget—take them, the seven who sniff like slaves at your heels. Let me name the other ten."

La Salle was wrathful. "Do it!" he roared. "Do it!"

Joutel said later that he was not surprised:

"Liotot, Duhaut, De Marle, our 'gentlemen of rank,' have smarted at having to obey commands. Hiens is a bully, Teissier a weakling. They were all ripe for some outburst. And there's L'Archevêque, Duhaut's valet, who is quite deranged with envy of Saget. I think, really, they'll be less of a menace in our group than if left at the fort. They might ferment such strife here that good Father Membré would be no match for them."

On January 7, 1687, early in the morning, the horses were loaded with gear and baggage, good-byes were said, and La Salle led forth his ill-assorted party. Though the day was gloomy and overcast, with a spatter of rain in the breeze, he was not discomfited.

Last night, Twelfth Night, he had stood with Saget and Nika, clinking mugs with them, shouting the appropriate toast: *"To the King! The King drinks!"* The little ritual had been bracing; the memory of it still warmed him. For that moment the three friends had fancied themselves back again in the blockhouse at

La Chine, the old times; and they had not minded that now the liquid in their mugs was cold water, not red wine from Father Queylus's cellar in Montreal.

Father Membré walked with La Salle; he would go only to the palisade. Father Membré seemed saddened at this parting; he walked with lowered eyes, fingering his rosary, his sandaled feet shuffling in the sand.

"You are heading due north, La Salle?"

"North and east. In two months, perhaps three, we should see the Mississippi."

"God willing." Father Membré's voice was husky. "God willing."

La Salle smiled. "You do not have faith in me?"

"Oh yes! Absolute faith. You must know that. And yet—"

"I wish I could tell you how positive I feel that at long last I'm on the right track."

"You deserve to be. You've been invincible. You are an honest man."

La Salle paused. They were at the palisade, where Father Membré must turn toward the fort, his small bereft flock.

"Once, in Rouen, old Father Guiscard called me that. He admonished me against the sin of ambition, selfish ambition. Would you say, sir, that I am guilty of the sin?"

"I would not say so, no." Father Membré raised his eyes; there were tears in them. "But if you were, I should absolve you of it."

"And you'll pray for me?"

"Always." A gust of wind ruffled the folds of Father Membré's shabby gray gown. He straightened them; then he embraced La Salle, kissing him on both cheeks. "Go now!"

"*Au 'voir*, sir."

"*Au 'voir*," Father Membré said. "May heaven bless you."

They marched rapidly, without mishap, fording many shallow gullies of muddy water, and reached the edge of a prairie where a herd of buffalo roamed. Nika stalked the herd and shot one huge beast; they feasted on the meat and made the hide into a boat. A river bisected the prairie; in their bull-hide boat they crossed, with the horses swimming behind, like dogs.

The weather changed; it was mild and sunny. The meadow grass rustled with the furtive scurryings of squirrels, rabbits, partridges, a variety of small game for their stewing kettles. Dotting the prairie were springs of fresh water, splendid camp sites, where one man could be stationed as sentry, while the others slept in a ring of firelight.

From the prairie they entered a dense woodland, sometimes treading paths smoothed by migrating buffalo, sometimes Indian trails. Almost daily they met Indians, hunters or fishermen, perhaps a whole tribe in migration. Usually the Indians were friendly, inviting the travelers to smoke the calumet with them. The influence which La Salle exerted over the uncivilized natives had never been more manifest. Because of him the entire party was received and entertained—though not all its members deserved such treatment.

Liotot and his faction were unpracticed; they had slight acquaintance with Indians, no understanding of them; they were discourteous guests in the pipe-smoking circles. But Crevel de Moranget was even more an offender. Crevel looked on the red man as his inferior. He could not approach one without condescension and rudeness.

Indeed, Crevel had become a problem to his uncles. Scarcely a day went by that he did not draw attention to himself. Privately La Salle and the Abbé Cavelier speculated on how he might be disciplined.

"It's not only that he quarrels with the savages," Jean said. "He argues with Liotot and Duhaut."

"They provoke him, taunt him."

"Yes, but our party is at best a queer thing, Robert, split by mutual suspicion and distrust. Why, it's two parties, made to have the aspect of one by your careful, impartial leadership. Underneath is dissension—and if ever it erupts, like a volcano, there will be an open feud between the surgeon's men and ours, perhaps a tragic feud."

"I wish Crevel were like Colin!" La Salle said. "He should pattern his conduct after Colin's."

"I told him so." Jean sighed. "He replied that Colin is a child, while he is an adult."

"Then let him act like an adult. I'll advise him—"

"No, Robert. Don't advise. Order!—as you would do with Saget, Nika, anyone else. I suppose that when you think of Crevel you are reminded of his mother. On Marie's account you're loath to be stern with him."

"Yes," La Salle said, "and I think of Crevel as he was in Rouen before my first voyage to America, a very little boy, all jelly-stained, mischievously running from his nurse. According to old Elise he was the image of my younger self."

"In countenance and stature he resembles you now. In character, not at all. For his own good he must be corrected—before it's too late."

"Too late?" La Salle frowned. "Why do you say that?"

Jean sighed again. "I don't know. . . . I don't know."

In March the party crossed the Brazos River and reached the waters of the Trinity River which were swollen to flood stage by spring rains.

Liotot balked at having to wade through ankle-deep mud. He said he would not budge from here until the flood receded. A week, a month—what difference did it make? They were but wandering, anyway. As on the *Joly*, they were without destination.

"I have my maps," La Salle said.

"Maps!" Liotot scoffed, in a tone reminiscent of Beaujeu's, and winked at Duhaut.

Though disgruntled, La Salle decided to appease the

surgeon; he told Saget to unload the horses and turn them out to graze; he made a campfire. But when the rains fell with renewed vigor, and steadily, for four days, he chafed and fumed inwardly. Coupled with that feeling, which still persisted, of being on the right track, the goal almost within his grasp, was a sense of pressure—to push on, to let nothing impede his progress.

On the fifth day of their halt beside the Trinity, the rain slackened.

"We will resume our journey," La Salle said.

"At your whim? Not I!" Liotot exclaimed.

But Saget rounded up the horses, La Salle's men marshaled into line—and reluctantly Liotot and his friends got up and followed.

FATEFUL MORNING

XVI

On March 15 they camped in a pine forest well beyond the flooded area. La Salle peered at his compass; he examined the trunks of the trees and saw that one was scarred with saber cuts.

He beckoned to Jean and Saget.

"We have been here before," he said. "On our excursion of last summer we spent a night under this pine; and we are only a few miles from that great oak with the hollow bole, in which we cached the sack of Indian corn and beans."

Jean nodded, and Saget declared that he could walk straight to the great oak in an hour or two.

Liotot was listening. "Your excursion of last summer?" he said. "You were looking for the Mississippi then, too—and not finding it. Yet today we are at the scene of that ignominious failure! What we do is to dance round and round, like white mice in a revolving cage, never getting anywhere. A degrading performance! But perhaps, Monsieur La Salle, the antics of white mice amuse you?"

La Salle disregarded his mocking inquisitor, aware that whatever he might have answered would be misinterpreted to discredit him. Every day Liotot was more critical; every day La Salle must quench the quick flare of his anger. But the open feud which Jean dreaded had not occurred, the volcano had not erupted. Gritting his teeth, La Salle had made innumerable concessions.

He spoke now to Saget: "I should be glad to have the cached food for extra rations. Go for it, you and Nika."

"And I'll accompany them," Liotot said promptly. "I am interested to see how these extra rations are apportioned among the weary little mice. I think Duhaut, Hiens, and Teissier would be interested, too."

"As you please, sir," La Salle said. "There is no one to oppose you."

Liotot summoned his three satellites and also L'Archevêque; with Saget and Nika they set out at noon.

At dusk Saget was back, alone. The corn and beans had molded, he said; they would be worthless as food. But Nika had flushed and killed two buffalo; the animals were being butchered:

"Liotot sent me for the horses, to fetch in the meat. He wants a couple of men to help with the packing— De Marle and one other."

Crevel de Moranget was standing near by. "I'll go, Saget."

"No," La Salle said. "You will not."

"Why?" Crevel demanded. "Why?"

"Because I'll not permit it."

"And why is that? Why do you always hedge me about with arbitrary restrictions?"

"For your mother's sake, and your grandmother's," La Salle said. "I must guard you—"

"Bah!" Crevel tossed his handsome head. "I'm a man and you shield and pamper me like a baby."

As La Salle still hesitated, Saget said: "It doesn't seem to me at all dangerous, sir. Liotot is in rare good humor, praising Nika for his skill as a marksman, clapping me on the shoulder. Duhaut, Teissier, they're in fine fettle, the lot of them, quite as if they'd got over their grudge and had a change of heart."

"There!" Crevel exclaimed. "You see how it is? You simply want to deprive me of a day's recreation! You are not fair to me. You and the Abbé Cavelier nag at me—"

"Crevel!"

"I am going."

"Go, then," said La Salle.

"We start in the morning," Saget said, and added apologetically: "I'm sorry, sir—but I'll look out for him; you mustn't worry."

At dawn the horses were harnessed; the three men mounted. The morning was cool and misty; and La Salle, who was watching the departure, noticed that, though De Marle and Crevel wore heavy coats, Saget's jacket was old and threadbare.

He pulled off his own blue woolen scarf, wadded it into a ball, and threw it. "Wrap this around your neck, Peter."

"Thank you, sir." Deftly Saget caught the scarf and, grinning, knotted it under his chin. He clucked to his horse. "We'll be back tonight," he said cheerfully.

The day seemed unnaturally long, suffused with a tension La Salle could not explain. For months he had kept both his nephews close beside him, literally within the range of vision; as Crevel said, he had hedged them about with restrictions, some of which were, perhaps, arbitrary and even absurd. And Colin had not complained.

"But Colin is a boy," he thought. "And Crevel is a man—in years, if not always in behavior. It's probably not to be wondered at that Crevel should rebel a little. . . . Saget was right: I must not worry."

Night came, but not the hunters. Wakeful, brooding, within reach of the sleeping Colin, La Salle lay on his bed of pine boughs and stared at the shadows.

"I have no cause for alarm," he thought. "Saget will look out for Crevel—he said so; I can depend upon it. And Nika is with them—"

Before his eyes flashed an image, of Nika, stalwart, bronzed, pausing at the door of an upper room of the Sulpician Seminary: "I will be your friend," Nika had said. . . . Well, that was long ago; but the pledge was good as new!

"I am a fool to worry," he told himself.

It was another day, slowly passing. The hunters did not come. In the evening he consulted Joutel:

"Why haven't they returned?"

"They've been detained," Joutel said.

"What could have detained them?"

"More buffalo. Or they have lost their way; the wood is full of thickets."

"Joutel, have you had any inkling of a conspiracy against me—against Crevel?"

"Oh, no!"

"Some hint? Think! Think hard; rack your brain!"

"I know of nothing."

"But what have you heard them say of me? Liotot? Duhaut?"

"Just what you have heard. Of course, they would say nothing more in my presence."

"They hate me! I know it—yet I have let my nephew, my sister's son, go with them. Tomorrow I'll bring him back."

"Take me with you tomorrow."

"No, Joutel. You stay with Colin, you and Jean. Father Douay can go with me. But lend me your gun and pistol; they're better than mine."

"Yes, sir; they're the best weapons in the party."

Strapping on Joutel's pistol, La Salle murmured: "It may be that the men have only lost their way."

During the night Indians straggled into camp. In the

stark gray light that precedes sunrise, he saw them squatting before the fire, rubbing their hands for warmth. He gave them something to eat and asked whether they could guide him through the forest.

"I have a shiny hatchet for some clever fellow."

One of the Indians jumped to his feet, grasped the hatchet and stuck it into his belt. Father Douay was dressed and ready; they went without good-byes of any sort, the Indian first, La Salle and the priest following after, silent and hurrying.

As the sun rose, Father Douay began to talk quietly of piety and grace, of the sacrifices and rich compensations entailed in the missionary's life.

La Salle felt soothed, reassured. The vague fears tormenting him for two days and nights seemed now without foundation. Forgetting them, he responded to Father Douay, telling him how God had enriched his own life—though he might repay his earthly debtors, he could never repay the debt he owed to God for His tender care and loving kindness.

Then he spoke of the meteor he had observed one winter at Fort Miami, far north on the St. Joseph. It had intrigued him, he said; he had never tired of gazing at it:

"And I thought, sir, that human existence is like a meteor, a bright arc emerging from darkness, vanishing in darkness, but known to God, necessary to His scheme, His infinite design for the universe."

"Ah, yes," Father Douay said. "Yes, La Salle, it is so."

They came to a small river, paused, and saw smoke spiraling from a clump of trees on the distant bank.

"The great oak is there." La Salle pointed. "And our men."

"And all is well!" cried Father Douay, rejoicing.

La Salle lifted his gun, meaning to fire it into the air. He lifted his eyes—and saw a pair of eagles wheeling in the sky just overhead.

He fired, waited for an answering salute, and got none.

A figure ambled into sight, on this bank of the little river, quite near. It was L'Archevêque.

"L'Archevêque!" La Salle shouted. "Where is my nephew?"

L'Archevêque stopped and stood, knee-deep, in the tall grass. He looked at La Salle, at Father Douay, but said nothing.

"My nephew! The young Moranget—where is he?"

L'Archevêque smiled waveringly. "The young Moranget? Well, he is here. Strolling about. Strolling—"

Panic clutched at La Salle's heart and squeezed it tight. He advanced one step, glanced down, and saw a blue woolen scarf in the grass—his scarf!—but wet and matted now with what must be blood.

"Saget! . . . Saget, Nika, Crevel! *Where are they?*"

Suddenly, terrifyingly, he knew where they were, stretched in the grass, with eagles wheeling above them.

He ran forward; and at that instant two guns barked, almost simultaneously.

He fell crashing to the ground, and Father Douay rushed to kneel beside him.

"La Salle! La Salle, what can I do?"

"Pray for me, pray for me—"

Incoherently, anguished, Father Douay prayed: "Hail Mary, full of grace . . . *Kyrie eleison.* Lord, have mercy. *Kyrie eleison* . . . May God remit unto thee the pains of the present and future—open to thee the gates of heaven . . . *Kyrie eleison* . . . Into Thy hands, O Lord, I commend this spirit . . . Holy Mary, Mother of God, pray for us sinners now and at the hour of our death . . ."

EPILOGUE

XVII

WHEN Father Douay, pale with horror, stumbled into camp, Jean Cavelier knew he must have witnessed some catastrophe.

"La Salle!" Jean cried. "My brother!"

"Dead—dead—"

In a low, quaking voice Father Douay told of the murder, how he had knelt and prayed over the fallen commander, how Liotot and Duhaut, guns still smoking, had got up from hiding in the grass to shout and gloat. . . . "There thou liest, tyrant! There thou liest!" . . .

"I was not even allowed to bury him," Father Douay said. "His poor, torn body was hurled into the bushes as carrion for the eagles."

Jean shuddered. "It was a conspiracy."

Yes, Father Douay said, a conspiracy—with a rapid, unforeseen climax. For weeks Liotot, Duhaut, and Hiens had wished to kill La Salle, but Crevel de Moranget's arrival at the oak-tree cache had precipitated the deed:

"Crevel and Duhaut quarreled, each wanting the best of the buffalo meat for himself. Then it was that Liotot resolved to kill Crevel also, and in so doing to set a trap for La Salle. Of course, good Saget and faithful Nika would have to be disposed of first. In the night, as they slept, these two were struck down with axes; then Crevel was murdered. This morning, as expected, La Salle came looking for his nephew and walked into the trap."

Father Douay had the story of the plot from De Marle, who had participated in it only because he was forced to. Now De Marle was remorseful—and the conspirators were returning.

"We, too, must die," moaned Father Douay.

"No!" said Jean. "Such criminal madness cannot triumph. We'll cling together, Father Douay—you and Joutel, Colin and I. An avenue of escape may be opened to us."

Liotot and his confederates were soon there. Swaggering and blustering, Liotot elected himself as new leader of the party and stationed Teissier to guard the priests, Colin, and Joutel. Teissier had never had any moral stamina; after half a day of guard duty he was weeping copiously and begging the Abbé Cavelier for pardon.

"What's to become of us?" Teissier wailed. "Liotot has no plan. Without La Salle we are lost indeed!"

A week dragged by; then Liotot announced that the party would march. This was the country of the Cenis Indians, and it was obvious that Liotot knew nothing of its geography. From village to village he went, asking about the Mississippi, being everywhere rebuffed. The German Hiens, who was wearing La Salle's clothing and flourishing Joutel's fine gun, growled that he, not Liotot, should be directing the march. Within a week the conspirators were in violent conflict among themselves. A week more, and Hiens had shot and killed Duhaut—and watched as Liotot died of a stray bullet through the lungs.

Though shocked and revolted, the priests and Joutel felt that with Hiens their captor the chance of escape had improved. Joutel talked with the German, asking for release.

"Free us, Hiens," Joutel said. "By this time you must see that we're more an encumbrance to you than a prize of conquest. We want to travel on, to the Mississippi, to Canada, finally to France. The boy Colin must be taken home, and some report made to the King of La Salle's assassination—"

"Ah, I'm innocent of that!" declared Hiens quickly. "I had no hand in it! Well, if the Abbé Cavelier will write out a certificate admitting my innocence, you may go."

Without quibbling over its falsities, Jean wrote out the certificate at once; for what mattered now—all that mattered—was to fly from the nightmare of treachery and bloodshed.

The travelers had La Salle's maps. Pursuing the route he had indicated, they marched northeastward and after eight weeks were at an Indian town on the Arkansas River where they met two of Tonty's men. These men, Couture and De Launay, said that in February, 1686, Tonty at Fort St. Louis had heard of La Salle's embarkation for the Gulf of Mexico and immediately had descended the Mississippi with a company to help with the establishment of his colony. In vain Tonty had awaited La Salle at the river's mouth; then he had gone back to Fort St. Louis, leaving Couture and De Launay on the Arkansas—for surely La Salle would come someday!

"No," Jean said; and, drawing Couture aside, he whispered to him.

"Alas, alas!" Couture bowed his head. "But this must be a secret from the Arkansas tribes! If told that the one white man they loved and trusted is dead, they might war upon us."

That night Jean said to Father Douay, Joutel, and Colin that perhaps it would be best to tell no one of their disaster until, safe in France, they could report to the King; and next day, in a canoe provided by Tonty's men, the little party launched on the Arkansas to paddle toward the Mississippi.

As they rounded into the great stream, Jean brushed tears from his eyes. He had found what his brother had sought so long, so indomitably.

"Robert was on the right track," Jean murmured. "He died believing that, and we have proved it."

Past the influx of the Ohio, past the Missouri they went, and into the Illinois, where Starved Rock reared imposingly. Landing at Fort St. Louis, they were cordially received—but Tonty was not there; Tonty was attending Indian ceremonials on the prairie. As they rested, waiting for Tonty, the travelers were subjected to much questioning about La Salle, to which Jean replied carefully, ambiguously.

In October, Tonty came, greeting them jovially, inquiring for his friend: "Where *is* La Salle? In the south? I suppose Saget and Nika are with him? They would never leave him, eh?"

"Yes," Jean said dully, with parrotlike inflection, "he's in the south. No, Saget and Nika would never leave him."

Tonty said it was strange he had not seen the colony. La Salle must have gone farther west; "But he would scarcely have pushed over into Texas, would he?"

"Texas?"

"The territory adjacent to Mexico which is now called Texas."

Jean was silent. He had no knowledge of Texas.

In March, equipped by Tonty, the travelers went on.

to Canada. By the middle of July they were at Montreal; six weeks later they boarded a ship for La Rochelle and home. In France, Jean wrote a full report of the tragedy, addressing it to Seignelay, who would transmit it to the King.

"Our glorious monarch, Louis the Magnificent, will act instantly," Jean predicted. "He will send a fleet to the rescue of Father Membré and those frightened, destitute souls on Matagorda Bay."

But Louis the Magnificent was singularly unmoved by the Abbé Cavelier's sorrowful tale. The Grand Enterprise of the Sieur de La Salle?—it had not prospered! Well, the King was only slightly out of pocket; he had not been to any degree inconvenienced; he had other things to think about—his fickle fancy was attracted elsewhere. He issued a warrant for the arrest of the assassins, should they ever reappear in Canada—and that was all. The episode was closed. . . .

In the autumn of 1688 Tonty was visited at Fort St. Louis by Couture and two Indians from the Arkansas. Now at last Tonty learned of La Salle's fate. Astounded and grief-stricken, he hastened down the Mississippi. Nothing could be done for La Salle, but his colonists might still be aided.

Tonty's search was thorough. He combed the forests along the river's banks; he sifted the Indian villages for miles around. It was a year before he relinquished the quest as futile. Then and always he mourned for La Salle.

"Robert Cavelier was the greatest man of his age,"

Tonty said. "He was one of the greatest explorers the
world has ever known." . . .

France and Spain were at war in 1689; Spain extravagantly claimed the Gulf of Mexico and all its coasts,
pressing with military might in every quarter. The expedition of the Frenchman La Salle had not gone unre-
marked. From the time when his ketch was plundered
off Santo Domingo, Spain had been vigilant. During the
next three years more information had seeped through
to Spaniards in Mexico, and Spanish sailors, scouring the
Gulf, had picked up bits of flotsam from the *Amiable*
and the *Belle*. But Matagorda Bay was in Texas, four
hundred miles west of the Mississippi; the secluded fort
there had never been sighted. Gradually the jealousy of
the Spaniards was lulled, the colony of La Salle almost
forgotten.

Now, in early spring, an army of Spanish guerrillas
from Mexico crossed the Rio Grande and, quite by accident, came upon a ruined settlement, hushed and tenant-
less, displaying no banners, the palisade shattered, the
dwellings reduced to heaps of rubbish. Through a litter
of crushed boxes and barrels, rusting utensils and implements, the Spaniards spurred their horses and saw no
living persons. But beyond, on the prairie, they encountered a small band of Indians—and the Spanish captain
jerked his horse to the halt.

"Seize that man! He's no Indian; he's a white man,
paint-smeared, disguised as an Indian."

Soldiers seized the cringing, paint-smeared white man.

"Who are you? What's been done to you?"

"My name is L'Archevêque," the man muttered. "I was with La Salle. We killed him—a mistake, wrong, very wrong; we knew it afterward. And Duhaut, my employer, was killed; and so I drifted again to the bay, the fort—"

The Spanish captain understood little of this. He flicked L'Archevêque with his riding crop. "You had a fort here?"

"La Salle's fort; he built it. Three months ago the Indians swept upon us, scalping, massacring. Some few of us were carried off as prisoners, but we crept back to bury the slaughtered. I myself buried fourteen of my comrades—and Father Zenobe Membré, our priest."

"You say La Salle was absent when the Indians attacked?"

"He was dead, I tell you!" L'Archevêque's eyes sparked with anger at the Spaniard's lack of wit. "Dead, or it would never have happened. The red fiends would not have attacked La Salle; he would have saved us—"

"You are my prisoner now; you'll be sent to Spain, a hostage." The captain frowned disdainfully and turned for one last look behind him. "There are no other survivors in that shambles?"

L'Archevêque shook his head. "No others, no others." . . .

BIBLIOGRAPHY

Cox, Isaac Joslin (Editor): *The Journeys of René Robert Cavelier, Sieur de La Salle, as Related by His Faithful Lieutenant Henri de Tonty; His Missionary Colleagues, Fathers Zenobius Membré, Louis Hennepin and Anastasius Douay; His Early Biographer, Father Christian Le Clercq; His Trusted Subordinate, Henri Joutel; and His Brother, Jean Cavelier; Together with Memoirs, Commissions, etc.* New York: A. S. Barnes and Company, 1905.

Lockridge, Ross F.: *La Salle.* Yonkers-on-Hudson, New York: World Book Company, 1931.

Parkman, Francis: *La Salle and the Discovery of the Great West.* Boston: Little, Brown and Company, 1931.

INDEX

American Indian Tribes, 26, 33, 53–54, 75, 83, 97–98, 100, 106–107, 167
Anticosti Island, 23
Arkansas River, 59–60, 105–106, 168

Baugis, the Chevalier, 115, 120
Bay of Quinté, 49
Beaujeu, Captain, 121, 127–132, 133–139, 145, 148

Canada, 2–4, 4–14; arrival of La Salle in, 24, 31, 36, 56, 88
Cartier, Jacques, 19; discovery of St. Lawrence River, 23
Catarqui, Iroquois settlement on Lake Ontario, 49; La Salle's seignory, 58–59, 63
Cavelier, the Abbé Jean, 2–3, 9, 24, 36–45, 70, 121, 124, 131, 137, 143, 149–169
Cavelier, Colin, 54, 122, 125–128, 143–168
Cavelier, Henri, 4, 7–12
Cavelier, Madame, mother of La Salle, 8–14, 53–54, 122
Cavelier, Paul, 8–12, 15–16, 53–54, 122
Cavelier, Robert, the Sieur de La Salle, birthplace, 5; home in Rouen, 6; education, 1–2; called La Salle, 5; ancestry,

5; first departure from France, 15–16; arrival in America, 24; first home in Canada, 31–37; first explorations, 38; discovery of Lake Ontario, 39; meeting with Joliet, 42; meeting with Frontenac, 48; assists Frontenac at Catarqui, 50–53; petitions King for seignory of Fort Frontenac, 53; meeting with Father Louis Hennepins, 56–57; plans expedition to mouth of Mississippi River, 61–63; starts for Mississippi, 68; builds the *Griffin*, 68; at Michilimackinac, 75–77; builds Fort Miami, 78–79; on Kankakee River, 81; on Lake Peoria, 83; attempt on his life, 86–89; holds council of Indians, 97–99; starts again for Mississippi, his party, 103; discovery of Gulf of Mexico, 109–111; plan to fortify the Mississippi, 112–114; audience with Louis XIV, granting of commissions, 120–122; departure from La Rochelle, 123–129; his ships, 123; route of voyage, 133–138; loss of the *Amiable*, 137; establishes

175

camp on Matagorda Bay,
140–141; last search for Mississippi, 148–162; death, 164
Champlain, Samuel de, founder of Quebec, 19
Colbert, minister of France, 63, 117
Courcelle, Governor of Canada, 22, 26, 33–35, 47, 49, 50

De Marle, 150–151, 158–159
De Soto, Hernando, 20, 29
Dollier, Father, 36, 38–45, 77
Douay, Father Anastase, 121, 124, 149, 161–169
Duhaut, 127–128, 141, 146, 150–167
Duschenau, 90, 115–116

English Channel, 17
English colonies in America, 19, 37

Fort Crevecoeur, building of, 85–86; destruction of, 90–92
Fort Frontenac, 53, 55, 69, 121
Fort Miami, 78–81, 97, 162
Fort St. Louis, on Illinois River, 113–115, 121, 168, 169
Fox River, 59
Franciscans, Order of, 17, 35
Frontenac, Louis de Buade, Count of Paluau and Frontenac, appointed Governor of Canada, 47, 48–54; council of Indians at Catarqui, 50–53, 60–65; attitude toward Jesuits, 71–72, 90–95,

98; recalled from Canada, 114; in France, 116, 119–120

Galinee, Father, 36, 38–44, 77
Green Bay, 59–60, 72, 75–76, 97
Griffin, the, planned by La Salle, 65; the building of, 69–77, 86; loss of, 90, 94
Gulf of California, 33
Gulf of Mexico, 59–60, 104, 109–110, 113, 117, 121, 134–139, 141, 145, 168
Gulf of St. Lawrence, 22–23

Hennepin, Father Louis, 56–57, 66, 69, 73, 79, 89, 97, 116
Hiens 127, 128, 141, 150–167
Hudson River, Dutch colonies on, 19

Illinois River, 60, 92, 113, 120, 169
Irondequoit Bay, 39
Iroquois Indians, the Five Nations, 26; Seneca tribe, 33, 53–55, 84; attack western tribes, 92, 94, 98

Jesuits, Order of, 2, 3, 9, 10, 30, 43, 45, 46–47, 70–72, 85, 101
Joliet, Louis, meeting with La Salle, 42–43, 48; explorations with Marquette to Mississippi, 59, 105
Joutel, Henri, 123, 131, 137, 141–142, 146–168

Kankakee River, 81–82, 93

La Barre, Febvre de, Governor of Canada, 114, 116, 119–120
La Chine, La Salle's seignory, 46, 48, 51, 71, 118, 152
La Forest, 66, 80, 94, 97, 113, 120
Lake Erie, 44, 74, 77
Lake Huron 75
Lake Michigan, 59, 75, 78, 90, 104
Lake Ontario, 39, 48, 95
Lake Peoria, 83–84, 91
Lake St. Clair, 75
Lake Superior, 42
Lake Winnebago, 59
L'Archevêque, 127, 151, 158–164, 171–172
La Rochelle, 67; La Salle's port of embarkation, 123–124
Laurentian Mountains, 23, 25
La Vantum, city of the Kaskaskias, 82, 113
Liotot, 127, 128, 141, 146, 149–167
Louis XIV, King of France, 3, 21–22, 47, 57; empowers La Salle to search for Mississippi River, 63, 110, 120–121, 168–169

Madeira, Island of, 129
Marquette, Father Jacques, 48; exploration of the Mississippi, 59; death, 60; mission at La Vantum, 82, 105

Matagorda Bay, 141–142, 148, 170–171
Membré, Father Zenobe, 74, 80, 89, 99–101, 106–107, 113, 121, 124, 137, 149, 172
Menominee River, 59
Michilimackinac, 68, 72, 75, 87, 97, 113
Mississippi River, 20, 30, 44
Monso, 84–85, 91
Montreal, 3, 18, 26, 27–29
Moranget, Crevel de, nephew of La Salle, 6–7, 12, 15–16, 54–55, 64, 122, 125–128, 143–164
Moranget, Marie Cavelier de, 6, 15–16, 54, 122
Moranget, M. de, husband of Marie Cavelier, 8, 12, 15–16, 54, 122

New France, 19, 95
New World, 2; colonization by European countries, 19, 20, 37
Niagara Falls, 42, 68–69, 72, 77
Niagara River, 42, 65, 68–70, 73
Nika, 27, 34, 45, 66, 113, 149; death of, 158–164
Normandy, 5

Ohio River, 33, 37, 39, 43–44

Prince de Conti, 64

Quebec, 3, 18, 23, 34, 48, 50, 70, 88, 115, 121

Queylus, Father, 28; Superior
of Seminary of St. Sulpice,
31, 35–36, 41–43, 152

Recollet (Franciscan) Order
of friars, 17, 21, 79, 91
Ribourde, Father Gabriel, 74,
79, 89, 99–101
Rio Grande, 171
Rouen, 1–2, 4–9, 27, 122–123

Saget, Peter, 112–114; accom-
panies La Salle to America,
16–29, 66, 113, 124, 149;
death, 158, 164
St. Clair River, 75
St. Joseph River, 78, 90, 93–94
St. Lawrence River, discovery
of, 23, 25–28, 34, 38, 68
St. Sulpice, Order of, 3, 36, 43
Santo Domingo, La Salle's
landing, 133, 171
Sault Ste. Marie, 45, 76
Seignelay, Minister of France,
117, 119, 121, 128, 139, 170

Seine, the River, 1, 17
Spain, possessions in America,
19, 37, 117, 171
Starved Rock, 81, 113, 169
Straits of Detroit, 45, 75

Talon, Jean, Intendant of
Canada, 22, 34–35, 42, 47,
60
Teissier, 127, 128; sinks the
Belle, 145–146, 150–167
Texas, 169, 171
Tonty, Henri de, La Salle's
lieutenant, first meeting, 64–
67; builds the Griffin, 73,
77–91; meeting with La
Salle at Michilimackinac,
97–102, 147; searches for La
Salle, 169–170

Upper Lakes, 43

"Vermillion Sea," 33

Wisconsin River, 59